The
IRONSTONE QUARRIES
of the
MIDLANDS

History, Operation and Railways

Part III
The Northampton Area
by
Eric Tonks
M.Sc., F.R.I.C., Dip.Maths.

Runpast Publishing

Cheltenham

© Eric Tonks

April 1989

Tonks, Eric S. (Eric Sidney), *1914-*
   The Ironstone Quarries of the Midlands:
   History, operation and railways.
   Pt. 3: The Northampton Area
   1. England. Midlands. Iron quarries, to 1980.
   1. Title
   622'.341'09424

   ISBN 1-870754-03-4

Produced for the Publishers by
Mopok Graphics
128 Pikes Lane
Glossop, Derbyshire
Printed in Great Britain

A busy scene in Blisworth yard on 30th December 1965. Hunslet locomotive 49 stands with empty wagons ready to push them to the quarry, while full wagons stand in front of *ETTRICK. BLISWORTH No. 1* approaches from the quarry, where the jib of the 5360 machine can be seen.

(G. H. Starmer)

CONTENTS

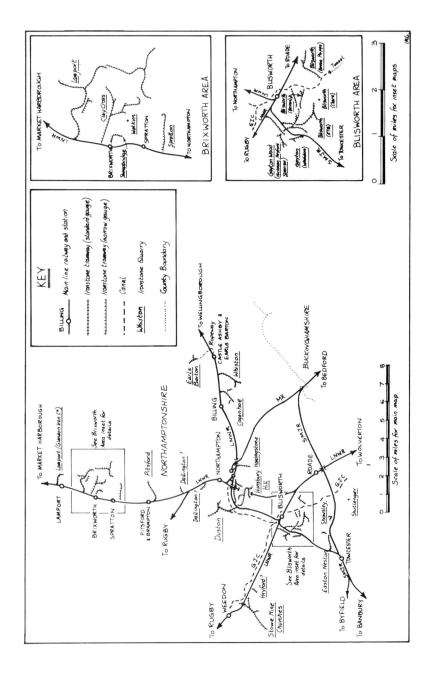

INTRODUCTION

The Northampton Area

Northamptonshire is the county most generally associated with the ironstone industry, with just over half of the quarries lying within its borders; it also boasts the longest history, starting earlier and finishing after the rest. Because of the bulk of the information to be dealt with, this has been divided into four parts, centred on Northampton, Wellingborough, Kettering and Corby. The first two cover broadly the Nene Valley, and the second pair the Ise valley and south of the Welland. Working tended to move from south to north, following the progress of railway building near the ironstone outcrops. There were ironworks in all areas, but here again the earlier ones were all in the south; they were mostly small and only Wellingborough survived the 1920's. All the quarries described in the four parts lie in the Northampton Sand formation, but it should be mentioned that there is a group of five quarries right at the southern tip of the county in the Marlstone Rock; geographically and historically these are more closely associated with the Marlstone quarries of the Banbury district and are dealt with along with them in Part II.

The area around Northampton may claim to be the cradle of the industry, with 9 of the 28 quarry systems commencing operations in the 1850s. The earliest quarries were close to the London & North Western Railway (LNWR) main line near Blisworth and the branch thence to Peterborough, and there was some use of the Grand Junction Canal; the LNWR Northampton-Market Harborough branch also tapped a rich ironstone area, and a few more quarries were served by the predecessors of the Stratford-upon-Avon & Midland Junction Railway (SMJR).

The earliest known ironstone quarry, at Hardingstone, was in being before Robert Hunt started to include ironstone in his *Mineral Statistics*, and several of the others had closed long before there was adequate recording, and it is difficult to imagine how they appeared — with unlettered quarrymen toiling long hours filling crude handworked tramway wagons. Others however had longer histories and there were new quarries opened in the 20th century that lasted to the twilight of the industry in the 1960s. Most of the older quarries were served by narrow gauge tramways, many with distinctive individual features, worked by horses or by locomotives. Apart from a small mine at Cogenhoe, all workings were opencast, and only quarries in production after 1900 had the benefit of quarry machines. Staveley opened up entirely new quarries at Lamport (1913) and Pitsford (1925), the former with narrow gauge tramways and an aerial ropeway, later replaced by a standard gauge line with a fearsome gradient; and there was a World War II revival of quarrying at Blisworth by Richard Thomas, so there was plenty to record. Some mysteries remain, as the text will reveal; we do not know for certain the site of the first quarry at Blisworth, nor where the Dallington quarries were, for example. We leave these for future historians with more time.

Some of the quarries had long or involved histories, making the task at once more difficult and more fascinating. Readers of *IRTM* will note a lot of changes to the information on these as a result of the greater amount of material now available in archives, notably in the County Record Office at Delapre Abbey, and the British Steel Corporation's East Midlands Regional Record Office at Irthlingborough; and the local researches of bodies such as the Northamptonshire Industrial Archaeology Group. Among local historians George Freeston of Blisworth is known nationally and has helped unstintingly over many years, while Len Bootman has an intimate knowledge of nearby Easton Neston; and there are many others who have contributed vital information of their own and from their knowledge of the right people to ask. All these are, I hope, acknowleged in the text. Personal friends to whom I owe special words of thanks are Geoffrey Starmer, who has given me the benefit of his wide knowledge of Northamptonshire in the course of a friendship extending over forty years (with a correspondence file to match!); Greg Evans, who took up the study in depth of the ironstone quarries in recent years and has passed on much valuable information obtained from former employees in the industry; Ian Lloyd, also keenly interested in the subject, for his excellent maps; and Martin Davies for his painstaking critical checking of the draft for style, grammar and clarity, and for his great efforts in copying archival photographs. Finally, I must thank the photographers who have kindly allowed the use of their work, without which this book would be much the poorer.

I was fortunate in seeing — just once — the archaic survival at Brixworth, with its pair of ancient locomotives and wooden tubs; I was told that it was then the oldest surviving ironstone tramway, which indeed it was — and looked it. I was given a footplate ride on *LOUISA*, and then sat on the bridge parapet, munching my sandwiches as the old Hudswell Clarke came rattling down from the quarry; how I wish I had had a camera to record this scene, so soon to cease. Such 'one off' experiences stay in the mind, for obvious reasons, while others capture the imagination for no well-defined reason at all. Whiston, for example; a small quarry with one locomotive, closed before I was interested in railways of any kind — yet the sight of the old loco shed perched on the skyline, and the well defined trackbed down the hillside somehow appealed to me. I did see the locomotive at Finedon, its name *WHISTON* betraying its origin. The history of this little quarry, as revealed in the archives, proved unusually complicated, justifying the interest aroused. Alas, there is precious little to see today.

For the very early quarries I have had to be content with visiting the sites and letting imagination do the rest—as you will have to do.

Birmingham 1989 Eric Tonks

Readers' attention is drawn to the explanation of abbreviations in the text and terms used in tables of locomotives and quarry machines, listed in pages 224-227

KEY TO INDIVIDUAL QUARRY MAPS

———————————————   Main Line Railway

BRIXWORTH   Station

+–+–+–+–+–+–+   Ironstone Tramway (Standard gauge)

·–·–·–·–·–·–·   Ironstone Tramway (Narrow gauge)

▪▪▪▪▪▪▪▪▪▪▪▪   Ironstone Tramway (Rope worked incline)

– – – – –   Canal

___⊥⊥___   Roads

Scaldwell   Village

Lamport Quarries   Ironstone Quarry

〜〜〜〜   Area of Quarry working

| Holcot | Quarry Face

↙ 1926 / 1932   Direction of Quarrying and dates of operation

SOUTHERN GROUP

To Blisworth goes the honour of having some of the first ironstone workings recorded in *Mineral Statistics*, which so faithfully chronicles the rise and fall of the iron ore industry in the 19th century; as we now know of other contemporary quarries not so recorded, any claims to be the 'first' ironstone quarry cannot readily be substantiated, but Blisworth was certainly among the earliest. Very fortunately, much valuable archival material came to light in the late 1970s, notably in Northamptonshire Record Office, to give us a much clearer picture of events in those formative years.

The existence of iron ore at Blisworth seems to have been revealed when the Grand Union Canal was cut about 1800, but there is no record of commercial exploitation until the 1850s; and although the London & Birmingham Railway had been opened past Blisworth in 1837, for more than half a century the canal played a vital role in the transport of ore from Blisworth, the only place where this was the case. The successive developments had a marked effect on the village; first the canal with its associated lengthy tunnel, then the high railway embankment forever cutting off the view across the flat fields towards Northampton, and finally the ironstone quarries on the villagers' very doorsteps. Today Blisworth has reverted to a quieter state apart from the heavy road traffic; it is still only a small place although it now houses commuters rather than agricultural workers. The canal is used mainly for pleasure craft, trains no longer stop, and the quarries have all been closed. The history of Blisworth has been the life work of George Freeston, and no one can study any aspect of the district without being indebted to him for his kindly and generous help. We shall have occasion to refer to him many times in this account of the quarries.

The neighbouring village of Gayton has an ironstone quarrying history of similar antiquity, and the quarries had the benefit of direct rail connection to the London & North Western Railway; but because *Mineral Statistics* tends to relate output to railway despatch points, Gayton was lumped in with Blisworth, and its comparable historical importance was to some extent unrecognised. In later years Blisworth, with its greater reserves, was the sole producer of iron ore.

BLISWORTH QUARRY

Owner: John Clare

Proposals to work ironstone both at Blisworth and Gayton were in progress early in 1852, the prime mover in the enterprise being John Deykin Clare, described as a Mineral Merchant of Yardley, Birmingham. Perhaps we can best introduce the dramatis personae of these negotiations by quoting from a letter dated 8th April 1852 discovered by George Freeston in, of all places, a Blisworth school document of 1845. The letter reads:

'... Mr. Clare is taking (with Mr. Woodhouse's sanction) several hundred tons of ironstone from Blisworth and is sending it to ironmasters in Staffordshire for trial. I think in about a fortnight he will be able to make some proposition for you and Mr. Woodhouse's consideration.

He has taken on Royalty the ironstone on Sir Hawley's property at Gayton which he says is of superior quality to any on the Duke's Estate.

I am, Sir

Your most obedient servant

John Simpson

John Simpson was Agent for the Duke of Grafton (the Duke referred to in the letter) and he was writing to John Parkinson, the Duke's legal adviser; John Thomas Woodhouse was Mr. Clare's solicitor, and Sir Joseph Hawley was Squire of Gayton Manor; the Gayton quarries, whose history is closely linked with those of Blisworth, are described later. As the letter states, Clare was already sending loads of Blisworth ore to Staffordshire for trial, and on the presumed successful outcome of these he commenced negotiations for a lease of the Duke's land; in this he joined forces with John Hickman, a coal merchant of Aston, also in Brimingham. The outcome of these negotiations is dealt with in the next section; but where did Clare get his trial loads?

The location is not specified, but one contender for this historic site is an old quarry on the south side of the Towcester road, about 300 yards southwest of the canal bridge where, alongside the hedge, is a clearly-defined quarry face about ten feet deep. The stones cannot tell us more, but if we move away from the noise of traffic rushing heedlessly past on the

Blisworth Quarry (Clare). The face of the quarry believed to have been worked by John Clare, looking towards the Towcester road. 29th October 1987. (Eric Tonks)

main road, tracing the outline of the quarry in the sunken field towards the quiet canal, we can ponder on the alternatives.

On a geological map in the BSC archives at Corby showing this site is the pencilled note '? Hickman 1853'. Hickman is a possibility, but he is definitely known to have worked on the other side of the canal, with a tramway tunnel under the Stoke Bruerne road, and would hardly have worked the west side as well. The only other company on this side is G. E. Bevan & Co, who worked ground to the west of the canal between the railway and the Towcester road from the 1870s to about 1900, but there has been no hint of their working south of the Towcester road. So, on balance, we will provisionally credit John Clare with this location. It is so close to the canal that it would have been simple to lay a tramway down the slope to the private wharf, but, if only trial loads were being sent from here, horse and cart to Blisworth Wharf would doubtless suffice. We will leave it at that, thankful that this leafy location has been preserved for us to examine and think about.

Grid Reference

723532   Quarry site

BLISWORTH QUARRIES

Owners: John Hickman: Blisworth Iron Stone Mining Co Ltd from 1859: G. E. Bevan & Co Ltd from 1861: Exors of Pickering Phipps from 1903.

As noted in the preceding section, John Clare and John Hickman were partners in an enterprise to extract iron ore from land at Blisworth owned by the Duke of Grafton; the draft lease preserved in the files was for a term of 21 years from 21st June 1852, with a royalty of 6d per ton of 22 cwt. The area is not quoted, but was about 200 acres, and was stated to comprise three areas — west of the canal; between canal, village and Courteenhall road; and between the latter and the railway, all with canal and rail access. This lease was apparently never put into effect; Clare's hopes of forming a company came to nothing and he decided to withdraw from the venture. In the Spring of 1853 he and Hickman mutually agreed to dissolve the partnership, leaving Hickman to carry on with the quarrying operations, possibly with another partner. The Duke however would not agree to grant the lease under this condition, though Sir Joseph Hawley at Gayton accepted it. Clare, it was said, had closer connections with the iron trade than Hickman, and the Duke would deal with no one other than a gentleman of similar experience and character. Hickman's operations were carried out by virtue of a two-year wayleave granted by the Duke early in 1852. The first trial loads of ore were sent to Staffordshire by canal, to which they were carried by tramway. The precise location of the quarry is not recorded but it probably lay east of the road to Stoke Bruerne, at the south end of the village. The selection of this site is curious; it was not the most conveniently placed because the tramway required a tunnel under the road in order to reach the canal. Perhaps the terms of the wayleave left no choice.

There is no contemporary account of this tramway but its location is confirmed in a letter from F. J. Farmer to John Simpson dated 26th August 1859, and it may be assumed to be the one used by the occupiers of the site. We were fortunate enough to be able to examine this tramway in a derelict condition on 19th December 1945; we did not then appreciate its antiquity and position as a pioneer ironstone line. Details of the tramway operation are given later, but in Hickman's day they would almost certainly have been simpler, probably with shovelling from wagon to barge — or, strictly speaking, 'narrow-boat'. In the quarry itself wagons were probably moved by hand.

Hickman realised the limitations of canal transport and at the beginning of 1853 applied to the LNWR for permission to provide rail connection to the quarries; but though the railway was so close, the topography was unhelpful and the only scheme acceptable to the railway company was an expensive one that involved alterations to the goods yard, and a tramway with an oblique bridge over the canal and a high embankment over the lower fields — all to be done 'with some regard to the eye' (letter 12th June 1854 from Hickman to Woodhouse; as an aside it seems that the railway company was unusually fussy about aesthetic values). This was far too expensive for Hickman to contemplate at the time and he continued to use the canal for loads sent to Staffordshire; even this was not without difficulties however, as freight rates by canal were higher than by rail, and few boatmen were prepared to accept the low prices Hickman could offer. As an alternative, he proposed to place the Blisworth ore on rail at his Gayton siding, paying Sir Joseph Hawley a wayleave of 2d per ton of the Duke's ore carried over the former's estate; in this way he hoped the trade could be built up sufficiently to justify the construction of the siding from Blisworth station, and asked the Duke for an extension of time from two to three years. Hickman appears to have been operating at Blisworth at least as late as October 1854, in which month Clare, in a letter to Woodhouse dated 16th October 1854, mentions his 'working the estate in a spirited manner... and spending much money on the property', so it would seem that the extension of time had been granted; but with the legal difficulties unresolved and the lease not yet put into effect, Hickman ceased work at Blisworth in 1855 (or possibly late 1854) and concentrated on Gayton quarries, (which see page 31).

Blisworth was undisturbed by the threat of further quarrying until 1859, when Mr. Whitton Arundell of Middlesex came into the picture. Who Arundell was, or how he came to know of the existence of ironstone at Blisworth, is not revealed, and after this one incursion into the industry he disappears into the shadows whence he came. He obtained a lease for ironstone and limestone on a 229 acre site for 21 years from 30th June 1859; full details of the lease are preserved, and the area involved seems to have been much the same as for Hickman except that there was no land west of the canal, but a larger area east of the main road, south of the railway.

Arundell commenced work under the style of Blisworth Iron Stone Mining Co Ltd and immediately ran into the same difficulties as his predecessor Hickman — transport. His solicitor, F. J. Farmer, wrote to John Simpson, the Duke's Agent, 26th August 1859.

'...Mr. Arundell says that (Field) No. 10 on the plan was to be included in his

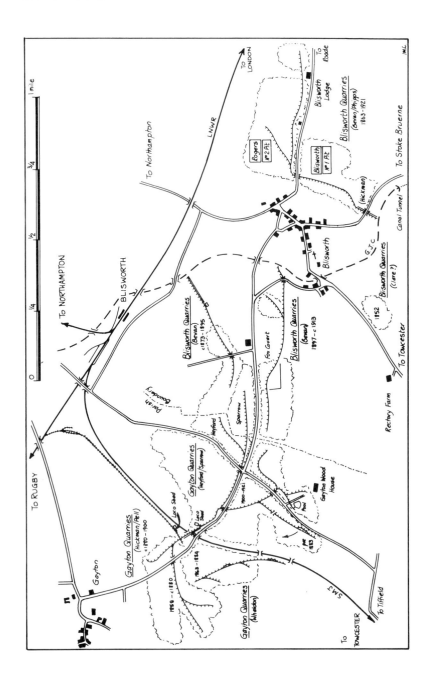

lease and it is essential to the working of the stone as it would enable him to get to the canal on that side of the land, and that there is a tramway running under the road to it from (Field) No. 212. In the reference it is called 'The Slopes' ... is there any objection to the piece of land being included in the lease? Mr. Arundell seems to make a point of it.'

With no other access, we cannot blame him and he evidently was granted the permission. Waterway Board records extracted by George Freeston reveal that on 21st October 1859 Arundell then sought permission, which was granted, to build a wooden bridge across the canal, from which the ironstone wagons could discharge their loads into a barge beneath.

Arundell received a contract to supply 300 tons of ironstone per week from 1st December 1859, rising to 1000 tons from 1st April 1860, and appointed a Mr. Billington as his agent on the site. He needed a siding from the LNWR and began negotiations with that company in the correspondence that forms the major part of the bulky file preserved in the Northamptonshire Record Office — and all to no avail. The railway company could see no way of introducing a siding on the Goods Department side and refused to entertain the idea of a tramway crossing the road between the Down platform and the hotel on the south side of the road. Arundell then suggested a siding off the Down line at the south end of Blisworth embankment, but the LNWR would not have this either; this was in March 1860 and the position was the same in July. Arundell had orders from South Wales but, as he wrote somewhat bitterly to Simpson on 3rd July 1860, 'without a siding the Duke's minerals are of little worth' and twenty railway trucks that he had hired were sent back unused after a month standing idle in Blisworth station sidings — with demurrage charges to add to his complaints! He got the railway company to cart some ore to the station but this idea was soon abandoned. It was still possible to send ore by canal to South Staffordshire but it was too costly, and some of the Staffordshire ironmasters who had expressed interest had gone out of business; South Wales was the market Arundell had hoped to develop and this he found himself unable to do.

The inevitable result followed soon enough in surrender of the lease in March 1861. 'Bridges, machinery and rails' were left in position for the benefit of a possible new tenant; for this role G. E. Bevan of Northampton (who was operating at Duston at this time) was recommended, and negotiations began in April 1861. The lease has not been discovered but it seems that Bevan very soon took over, as just two years later he was sending away considerable quantities of ore by a novel transport system (see *Mining Journal* 18th April 1863, p.268). He had already had some experience of

Blisworth Quarries (Hickman/Bevan/Phipps). Drum windlass with loaded trucks waiting to be lowered down to the canal, and then hauled up again. The lady is from the 'New Buildings' and is collecting water from the shallow well — the only supply. c 1910.

(W. Alexander)

difficulty in making arrangements with the LNWR and wasted no time in pursuing the same course as his predecessors at Blisworth; instead, after a short period of sending ore to the station in carts, he reopened the tramway and incline down to the canal, along which the ore was sent no further than Blisworth station. The tramway was of 3ft. 7in. gauge and horses were used for moving wagons from the quarries to the head of a cable-worked incline, where the cable was wound round a drum mounted over the rails; at the foot of the incline a timber bridge carried the tramway across the canal. There was a gentle slope between the Courteenhall Road pits and the drum, and wagons waiting their turn had an oak 'sprag' thrust between the wheel spokes by the brakesman (who was usually known as 'Sprag'). The wooden wagons had slightly flared sides rather higher than was common practice in contemporary ironstone systems, and were end-tippers; each loaded wagon was attached to the cable and allowed to run to the far end of the bridge, where one end of the wagon was raised by means of a jib, and the contents were shot through a gap in the planking into removable tubs in a barge below. At the railway station Bevans laid a set of sidings on the canal wharf and installed a steam crane to lift the tubs and deposit the contents into railway wagons. The output at first went to Staffordshire (by water), Derbyshire and South Wales (by rail) but by 1865 went almost wholly to South Wales (Plymouth Ironworks; Golynos; Tredegar; Abersychan etc). The driver of the donkey engine of the crane was a Mr. Massey, who kept the despatch books; the counterfoils were then used by his daughter as scrap paper for recording recipes and laundry lists, and she gave the remaining three to George Freeston, from whom this information came. The main line wagons held mostly six tons of ore, and the weekly output was about 1000 tons.

A Blisworth Vestry Meeting of 30th May 1884 records the length of the tramway as 43 chains and 28 links. There were two quarries: one at the top of the incline and another north of the Courteenhall road, to reach which a brick-lined tunnel was built. Records for royalty payments for 1864 refer to No. 1 Pit and No. 2 Pit, which presumably are these two pits respectively; but by 1874 they were referred to as Blisworth Pit and Roper's Pit, and by 1879 as No. 1 Quarry and Roper's Quarry. Royalties varied between 4d and 6d per ton. These records are in the Northamptonshire Record Office.

Blisworth Quarries (Hickman/Bevan/Phipps). View of quarry north of Courteenhall Road, looking east from the bridge. c 1900.   (Collection George Freeston)

Blisworth Quarries (Hickman/Bevan/Phipps). Looking east from canal bridge towards the tunnel under Stoke Road. Note the cable from the drum just visible through the tunnel. Photograph taken on a day when the line was not working evidently! c 1910.

(Collection George Freeston)

Blisworth Quarries (Hickman/Bevan/Phipps). View from canal towpath, looking south, showing the bridge with an ironstone wagon near the crane and the chute for filling barges. Side-tipping limestone wagons on the quayside. Sunken barge (the object of the photo) in front. c 1916.

(Collection George Freeston)

In April 1899 Bevans acquired a new quarry site to the west of the canal (see below) as they 'expect to be worked out at the old pit near Blisworth Tunnel in six month's time' (Waterways Board Records letter 10th April 1899). Operations at the new site apparently commenced on schedule, and Bevans vacated the old one. There was still ore to be had however and the quarries were taken over by the executors of Pickering Phipps of Hunsbury Furnaces. Phipps obtained permission to use the limestone landing stage near the tunnel mouth on 26th November 1903 (BSC records) and presumably commenced operations then or very shortly afterwards—though the terms of the lease have not come to light—using the same method for despatching the ore. It seems likely that the barges plied directly between Blisworth and Hunsbury Furnaces, as a result of which there must have been some congestion of the canal, and in the summer of 1908 the Grand Union Canal dug a new 'winding hole' for turning barges at Hunsbury. At a later period there was a revival of Bevans' method, when the barges were unloaded at the wharf at the south end of Blisworth station, where a short siding was laid from the LNWR; here a crane was kept for raising the tubs, the bottoms of which were then opened and the contents dropped into railway wagons for transit to Hunsbury. The latter arrangement overcame the delays occasioned by fifteen locks between quarries and ironworks. The barges were about 71ft. long, 7ft. wide and 4ft. deep, and held 25-30 tons of ore.

Though this was one of the very first ironstone tramways, it was considerably predated by another tramway just to the south, but which was exclusively used for carrying limestone from a quarry on land belonging to the Duke of Grafton. The quarry was opened up in 1821 by John Roper, the Duke's agent, and the tramway was laid in the same year in the form of a tramroad.[1] The executors of Pickering Phipps obtained a lease of tramway and quarry, comprising three fields and a portion of a fourth, for 11¼ years from 29th September 1902, and from then onwards the two tramways, ironstone and limestone, were operated as one unit; it may have been in this period that edge rails replaced the original tramplates on the limestone line. This latter ran to the same wharf as, but did not make physical connection with, the ironstone line, and its gauge is not certain, though photographs suggest that it was the same as its confrere. Operating methods were different, however; wagons were braked down to the wharf, and empties were hauled up by horses, which were also used for quarry work. The wagons were wooden side-tippers, discharging their loads via a wooden chute on the canal bank into waiting barges. A brakesman travelled on the trucks and could pull them to a halt if necessary. A boy was employed at Stoke Road crossing to give permission to cross; a switch point existed 50 yards east of the road and, if operated, the trucks were simply derailed. The limestone quarry was said to have been closed 'about 1912' — probably when the lease terminated at the end of 1913. In 1920, however, new leases were enacted in respect of both ironstone and limestone quarries, both for 28 years from 25th December 1919, at a royalty of 4d per ton for ironstone (both quarries) and a wayleave of 1d per 'ton' of 2460 lbs; the ironstone area was the large field of 30 acres south of Courteenhall Road, leased from Harry Perkins (presumably the occupier) and the Stone Works quarries of 24½ acres from John Thomas Lepper.

The everyday work of the quarries was a purely manual affair, and was described to George Freeston by William Perkins; we give similar recollections for quarries elsewhere, as they differ in detail according to the teller. Men who did the 'unbaring' (removing overburden) were paid 4d per yard; digging was straightforward, but 'running the plank' with a loaded barrow was quite a skilled job. In earlier days 11in. pitch pine planks were used and it was essential to keep step with the bouncing of the plank; in 1919 new regulations required 15in. planks when 'it felt like walking the deck of an ocean liner'. Occasionally a 'dead' plank that did not spring was

Blisworth Quarries (Hickman/Bevan/Phipps). Bridge over canal to loading stage on the west bank. The continuation of the line south along the canal bank was used by wagons from the limestone quarries. c 1930. (Collection George Freeston)

met with; the men hated them, as they sagged in the middle and tended to come off the trestles (or 'trussels' as they were called). Wages came to 25—30 shillings per week.

The ironstone quarries ceased to work on 1st January 1921, in line with the blowing out of Hunsbury Furnaces; the men received verbal notice without warning, and everything was left exactly as it would have been at a normal weekend in expectation of restarting on Monday. Most of the equipment was allowed to go derelict on the site, the most remarkable exhibit being a wagon standing on the bridge over the canal; it remained thus, on rails suspended in mid-air, long after most of the timbers had rotted away (to the annoyance of boatmen) for the best part of twenty years. Three ore boats were left tied up at the landing stage, but were broken up in 1927, according to canal company records. Most of the track and usable scrap was salvaged in the early years of World War II, though a couple of wagons were left behind until 1943 or a little later. These were of the high wooden side-tipping type favoured by contractors in the late 19th century, and which were to be found in many quarries. They were probably used for waste disposal in the quarry itself and may have come from the limestone pits, of course.

Richard Thomas & Co Ltd acquired Hunsbury Ironworks and their associated quarries as from 30th September 1935, including Phipp's site at Blisworth, which passed to Richard Thomas & Baldwins Ltd, as recorded on an unusual notice over their name — 'Any person found depositing rubbish on these allotments or in the disused ironstone tramway will be prosecuted'. The years have whittled away the visible remains. The bridge over the canal went early on, but in the middle 1950s traces of the cable drum remained, and also some of the rails, half buried in the quarry, together with a pair of wheels. The lease expired 25th December 1947. In the early 1960s part of the ironstone quarry area was filled in and bungalows and houses built on the site—though the early subsidence of walls revealed that the filling had not been very expertly carried out! The notice board referred to above disappeared about the same time, but the tunnel under Stoke road was still extant and almost completely choked by undergrowth. In November 1976 it was filled in by a novel means—some 400 tons of dry mixed ballast and cement were blown in until the cavity was filled, the mixer and compressor being located on the road above; the west end of the tunnel was then banked with loads of soil. A plot on the east side was purchased in 1982 and incorporated into a garden, and the road wall was repaired.

The bridge under Courteenhall Road was filled in in October 1982, and

Blisworth Quarries (Hickman/Bevan/Phipps). Bridge under Stoke Road, c 1950. This is now filled in. Cable drum support can be noted. (George Freeston)

consists of ironstone blocks on top of a double red brick lining. The course of the final tramway line north of the road is still partly traceable, with the north hedge intact as far as the house 'Longmead', forming part of a private garden. The quarrying area extended for about 200 yards to the north of the road, where the ground falls away towards the BR main line; at the roadside it is marked by a steep drop in level which skirts 'Longmead' and stretches as far as Blisworth Lodge, and there is also a further quarried area north of the Lodge. Which portions were worked by Bevan and which (if any) by Phipps we do not know.

South of Courteenhall Road the area is below road level also but there has been some filling for house foundations, and the tunnel mouth (at the rear of No. 18 Wellspring, off Windmill Avenue) has been filled almost to the top. There is however a gullet in the allotments. Of the stone side pillars that once supported the drum there is almost nothing to be seen, but in the gullet at this point is a modern brick pillar with a manhole and cast iron inspection lid, for a surface water pipe from the Courteenhall Road houses to the canal, laid along the gullet bottom. The inspection cover is at the

Blisworth Quarries (Hickman/Bevan/Phipps). Tunnel under Courteenhall Road from the south side. The tunnel has now been filled in and ground in front is a private garden. c 1965. (George Freeston)

25

level of the surrounding land. At the canal bank the embankment leading to the bridge can be seen and on the far bank is the ledge where the limestone sidings were.

The limestone gullet at the back of Stone House was bulldozed in 1967 so that the land could be restored to farm use, and Mr. Cherry, the owner of the fields, turned up several pieces of tramplate rail, one marked CC, indicating that it came from the Blisworth Canal Tunnel Tramway, where the rails were marked GJ at one end and CC at the other (Grand Junction Canal Company). Presumably these rails formed the original track of the quarry line. The limestone quarry itself, though overgrown, remains open. During 1980 there was a scheme to use the limestone quarry in connection with repairs to the Northampton section of the M1, with the installation of machinery to recycle M1 material for reuse and dump the waste in the quarry. After many protests these plans were scotched, but it is still suggested that the quarry be filled in and restored to farm use. The land belongs to Sir Hereward Wake.

Blisworth Quarries (Hickman/Bevan/Phipps). Site of final gullet north of Courteenall Road, c 1965. The site has been much altered since but is still recognisable.

(George Freeston)

Footnote

1.   For a fuller account, see 'Quarry line at Blisworth' by George Freeston, and included in *Rails over Blisworth Hill*. Compiled by Victor Hatley. Northampton Historical Series, No. 2; second edition, 1970.

Grid References

727531	Canal bridge
728532	Bridge under Stoke road
730535	Bridge under Courteenhall road
732535	Quarry terminus

BLISWORTH QUARRIES

Owners: G. E. Bevan & Co Ltd: Exors of Pickering Phipps from 1901

Where the ridge of high ground further to the northeast of Gayton sloped down to the Grand Junction Canal about half a mile north of Blisworth tunnel, the outcropping ironstone at the summit was worked in the late 19th century by G. E. Bevan & Co Ltd; this area had been included in the original 1852 draft lease to Clare & Hickman, but excluded from the 1859 lease to Arundell. As already stated, Bevan's lease has not come to light; previous history suggests a comprehensive lease including areas on both sides of the canal, but on the other hand Bevan may have negotiated for the eastern pit only in 1861, and later a further lease in respect of the western side. The date when operations commenced here is also unknown, as MS simply records G. E. Bevan & Co Ltd at Blisworth without discrimination between the two sites; opening was probably about 1873 (per BSC files) and the 1883 6in. OS shows a tramway between pits and canal, the despatch arrangements being the same as those for Bevan's other Blisworth quarries.

The tramway ran down the hillside to the canal close to Blisworth station. Traces are to be seen of the line from the shallow pits bordering the farm at the top of the bank, beyond which it is presumed the tubs were lowered to the wharf by a rope-worked incline; the 1883 OS shows a building at the summit and — rather intriguingly — a 'signal post'. In *IRTM* it was presumed that the building was a winding house, but George Freeston states that the barn was there long before the tramway and had no connection with the ironstone operations; it was demolished in 1978 by the farmer. Nothing is known of the gauge nor of the type of wagon employed, but they were probably not the same as at the company's other Blisworth pits, where they used end-tipping wagons opening over the canal boats. There is no evidence of such a system here; possibly side-tipping wagons running along a short wharf were used, or even shovelling between wagons and barge.

It is not known when this system ceased work, but the tramway is not shown on the 1900 6in. OS; by this time the stone north of the Blisworth-Gayton road in the vicinity of the farm had been removed, and the Fox Covert Pits on the south side were opened up, a new tramway being laid from them to the canal. On 10th April 1899 Bevan's applied to the Grand Junction Canal to 'place an ironstone landing' in the canal about ten feet long, projecting some five feet into the waterway; this was clearly to allow

Blisworth Quarries (Phipps). Tipping stage on canal bank, showing removable tubs in barge being filled from wagons. Note the horse used for pushing wagons along the stage. This was the second canalside stage used by Phipps. c 1900. (Collection George Freeston)

them to use the system they had at their quarries east of the canal, which they expected to be worked out in six month's time. It seems likely, therefore, that some of the equipment — rails, wagons etc — were transferred from the old site, though in this case no rope-worked incline was required. The tramway had a gentle downhill run and at the canal end, where the ground fell away sharply, ran on an elevated wooden staging, in the floor of which was a chute leading to the berth for barges beneath; wooden wagons with flared sides and opening at the end were braked down to the stage, on to which they were pushed by horses, and their contents shot into tubs in the barges. The barges then took the empty tubs back to the pits; the latter were quite close to Sparrow's old workings and in fact at one point two excavated fields were separated only by a narrow wall of stone supporting a straggling hedge, the parish boundary between Gayton and Blisworth. These quarries did not last long and seem to have been closed just before World War I.

There is not much to be seen at the sites of the tramways today; a depression across the fields is all that remains of the earlier line. It had passed under a 'green lane' behind the farm; the 'green lane' has gone, and the bridge too, but the dip in the ground is there. Of the second tramway there was (1981) hidden by the canal bank greenery, a wooden pile about three feet out of the water, flanked by two smaller and badly eroded piles, one on each side, where the stage used to be, and gate posts at the level crossing. Nearby are wooden buildings that were the workshops of C. Burbidge, a local builder and repairer of agricultural machinery — later E. J. Burbidge — but now serving as poultry sheds. It is possible that these were the former stables for the horses used on the ironstone tramway.

The quarrying area extended as far as the Blisworth-Gayton parish boundary, beyond which Sparrow held the lease; south of the road, the boundary hedge, quarried away on each side, still remains untouched at its higher level. Eastwards from this hedge the former quarried area is indicated by low level ground to within 200 yards of the farm (but on the south side of the road, of course) with a further isolated quarry in the angle between the roads to Blisworth village and Blisworth Wharf.

Grid References

First site
725542	Canal tip
722541	Top of incline
719539	Green lane crossing by farm

Second site
724536	Canal tip
723536	Level crossing

Blisworth Quarries (Phipps). Probable stables near the level crossing. 9th January 1979.

(Eric Tonks)

GAYTON QUARRIES

Owners: John Hickman: Pell & Co from 1858 (?); Heyford Iron Co Ltd from March 1874: R. B. Sparrow from 1900.

These quarries were contemporaneous with the first Blisworth quarries, and negotiations were conducted in 1852 by the same lessees, John Clare and John Hickman, with Sir Joseph Henry Hawley, Bart, the owner of Gayton Manor (though then living in Kent) and with Thomas John Butcher of Penzance. The status of Butcher is not clear — possibly he had a lease on the Manor House; he leased 51 acres of land, occupied by John Manning Payne, to John Deykin Clare and John Hickman for 7 years from 10th June 1852. The other lease was between Sir Joseph Hawley and Clare and Hickman for 21 years from 6th July 1852, the area not being stated. It will be noted that the Butcher and Hawley leases were respectively dated 11 days before and 15 days after the Blisworth lease. As described under the Blisworth section, Clare and Hickman dissolved their partnership in 1853, and while the Duke of Grafton refused to grant a lease to Hickman alone, Sir Joseph had no such reservations and in 1854 formally consented to the existing arrangements; further, a second lease was enacted to run for a further 14 years from 10th June 1859; in this case the lessors are quoted as T. J. Butcher and Sir Joseph Hawley, and the area was 48 acres. This contained provisions common to many leases of the period, e.g. there was to be no 'mining' (quarrying) within thirty feet of any building, and royalties were fixed at 4d per ton of raw ironstone, or 5d per ton if calcined. There was also a proviso that three months were to be allowed after determination of the lease to remove sidings and tramplates, implying that a tramway was in use.

The documents in the Northamptonshire archives do not include a map showing the ground leased, but there can be little doubt that it was in the same general area as the later quarrying activities at Gayton, which were on both sides of the little valley between Gayton and Blisworth villages. A three-quarter mile standard gauge tramway was laid along the valley to a junction with the LNWR a quarter of a mile west of Blisworth station, and from the head of it to the workings there was doubtless a narrow gauge tramway worked by hand or horse.

We do not know when Hickman commenced production at Gayton, but it was probably 1853, as the main line connection was in use by then, and Hickman was considering it for the despatch of Blisworth ore. *Mineral Statistics* is not much help for this period, the details being only fragmentary. The first record of ironstone from the East Midlands is for 1855, which merely quotes 'Weedon, Northampton and Blisworth' with no quarry owners' names given, but a combined output of 74084 tons, suggesting that all sites were under common ownership — which, if so, must be George Pell. The same three locations occur in 1857 (Northampton is omitted in 1856) and Pell & Co's Heyford Ironworks appears for the first time. In 1858 the only quarries given are:

Gayton (Pell & Co) ... Output 75000 tons
Gayton (J. Hickman)... Output   3395 tons

Under the 1858 entry for Heyford Ironworks appears the note 'supplied from Gayton'. This could imply that in the previous year the works was supplied from elsewhere, possibly — though not necessarily — Scowe. It is however reasonable to assume that the locations given in 1855/6/7 are the stations from which ore was despatched, whereas Gayton is an actual quarry and was presumably the source of ore despatched from Blisworth station in 1855/6/7. Pell might have worked part of the same area as Hickman through some private arrangement, as he did with G. E. Bevan at Duston; certainly it seems that they worked together to some extent and that as Hickman moved out, Pell moved in. MS quotes Hickman and Pell as operating individually at Gayton in 1858/9, but in 1860 records a single combined output of 67818 tons from four quarries—Desborough and Gayton (Hickman) and Duston and Gayton (Pell). According to Hewlett, Hickman opened quarries at Desborough shortly after the Midland Railway arrived there in 1857, and his workings were later taken over by the Stanton Ironworks Company, Hickman becoming their agent or manager; also, in 1867, Stanton started to receive ore by canal from Gayton — possibly as a result of a recommendation from Hickman?

Either under his own name or that of Heyford Iron Co (of which he was the proprietor) Pell continued to work the quarries, which were shallow opencast pits disposed along both sides of the valley between Gayton and Blisworth, with tramway connection to the standard gauge terminus. The Northampton & Banbury Junction Railway, opened in 1873, used this same valley to gain access to Blisworth station, but near the head of the valley their line took a southwards curve in deep cutting, clear of the ironstone field then being worked a third of a mile southeast of Gayton village, and west of the road to Blisworth. By the time of the 1883 6in. OS these quarries had been abandoned, but work continued east of the road. In the later 19th century quarrying was concentrated more on the east side of the N&BJR

Gayton Quarries (Sparrow). Quarry view, near the crossroads c 1905. A typical example of early quarrying practice. The man standing at the top is Fred Nightingale of Pattishall, and two other members of the family are present in the group, who were identified by Charles Rooke of Gayton in 1979. (Collection George Freeston)

(later SMJR) line, both north and south of the road connecting Gayton and Blisworth villages. All traffic continued to go out via the LNWR connection, and a tramway network was laid to serve the various workings; these lines converged at tipping chutes alongside the standard gauge tramway from the LNWR that paralleled the SMJ for much of its length. Eventually the narrow gauge line was carried east towards Blisworth, tunneling beneath the Rothersthorpe-Tiffield road south of the crossroads.

The ore was loaded by hand into small end-tipping wooden tubs that were hauled by steam locomotive from the easterly workings to the head of a double incline worked by endless cable, with descending full wagons hauling up the empties. The incline was just east of the N&BJR, crossing the latter, when it came to be built, by a wooden bridge; the tubs from the western pits were hauled by horses to the tipping chutes. It is quite possible that the line to the eastern pits was horse-worked originally. The company also maintained a locomotive to haul the standard gauge wagons from the chutes to the LNWR, together with horses to perform shunting operations at Gayton while the engine was down at the junction.

After Heyford Ironworks closed in 1891, it appears that quarrying for ironstone continued — or at least, that ironstone was disposed of, possibly from stocks on the site—and LQ for 1895 includes 'Heyford Brickyard, Gayton' owned by the Heyford Iron Co Ltd, with an output of 18000 tons. By 1900 this had dwindled to 9000 tons and in 1901/2/3 the quarries are described as 'standing'. Presumably a brickworks had been established here while the ironworks was still working, and certainly there was one in later years under the style of Blisworth & Stowe Brick & Tile Co Ltd, to which we shall have occasion to refer later. The small stream in the little valley along which the standard gauge line ran was culverted in bricks, an unusual refinement for a small line, but doubtless because bricks were made on the spot.

In 1900 the quarries were reopened by R. B. Sparrow, who worked the system until 1921, when the outcropping ironstone was practically exhausted. Sparrow is well remembered—for example by George Freeston and Mr. C. R. H. Simpson—as he was a remarkable looking man, about 6ft. 3in. tall, very broad, and with a strutting kind of walk 'rather like a stork'; he lived at Blisworth House, rented from the Duke of Grafton, but as this was sold vacant in 1920 it is possible that Sparrow was not in charge at the end of operations. Sparrow's name does not appear in LQ, but there was no statutory obligation for this unless the workings exceeded a certain depth; GSM records 4-5ft. of overburden and 5-6ft. of ironstone. However, as Heyford Iron Co Ltd was still quoted up to 1903 (albeit 'standing', i.e. idle) it would seem that Sparrow only used a portion of the quarrying area, on the Blisworth side. It was rumoured that another company sought to obtain access to the orefield by means of a line connecting with the SMJR south of

Gayton Quarries (Sparrow).
R. B. Sparrow in person, in front of one of his own wagons. c 1905.
(Collection George Freeston)

the Gayton-Blisworth road, but was unable to come to terms with the then owners. The SMJR board minutes of 14th February 1912 state that T. & I. Bradley Ltd of Darlaston had obtained a lease of about 200 acres, and were requesting a siding on the SMJR between the Blisworth-Gayton road bridge and the next bridge; it was said that they had an excavator and intended to calcine. It seems probable that these two pieces of information are related, as the site must surely be the same one; but nothing came of these proposals.

Local testimony of the history of the 1900-21 period is far from unanimous, but it seems probable that when the Heyford Iron Co Ltd ceased quarrying (or when the ironworks closed, perhaps) the standard gauge locomotive was disposed of and the rest of the system left much as it stood, including the locomotive and wagons on the narrow gauge portion. This was taken over by Sparrow; he did not reintroduce locomotive power on the low-level (standard gauge) section but used horses, each animal taking three loaded wagons at a time to the LNWR at 'Gayton Loop'; the SMJR also put in a siding near the overbridge, and a chute was installed so that the ironstone tubs could be emptied into their wagons. According to information kindly supplied by A. St. G. Walsh, the SMJR working timetable for October 1912 does not record this siding, but that of January 1916 does, so it was probably a wartime measure. Full details of the narrow gauge tramway and rolling stock have escaped record, a pity in view of their antiquity and doubtless highly local character; but an idea can be obtained from the photographs taken about 1905 and supplied by Mr. Charles Rooke of Gayton, who identified the men depicted. The gauge of the tramway is said to have been about 2ft. 10in., which seems not unreasonable, though perhaps a trifle wide, judging from the fairly extensive traces of the former lines that were visible in the 1950s and which included a few rotting sleepers, 4ft. 9in. in length, in cutting to the western pits. The locomotive was a four-coupled saddle tank named *GAYTON* that did not survive to the closure, having been replaced shortly before by a four-wheeled petrol locomotive, said to have been built by Groom & Tattersall, the engineering firm of Towcester. Mr. L. V. Bootman recalls that this company's predecessors, M. W. Groom & Son, had built such a machine, using a Darracq or a De Dion Bouton car engine, about 1919 — which may well have been the one concerned. The origin of *GAYTON* is not known, but it is believed to have been locally built also.

The areas specifically worked by Sparrow are not known with certainty, but obviously he had to extend the tramways, and on the north side of the Gayton-Blisworth road appears to have crossed into Blisworth parish to open up an area south of that formerly worked by G. E. Bevan; the parish boundary hedge (left intact south of the road) was breached here to allow access for the tramway.

All quarrying operations were by hand, and the ore was sometimes calcined at the pit; the latter suggests that the ore was sent some distance, borne out by a statement in GSM of customers in Yorkshire, Shropshire and Staffordshire. Some of the ore was riddled, for what purpose is unclear. When work ceased in 1921 at the onset of the slump in the iron trade, much of the equipment was left as it stood; and on 10th June 1925 an auction was held by Messrs Jackson Stops at Gayton Wood to dispose of 101 eight-ton and 10 ten-ton standard gauge wagons. Of these the 'converted' type were built mostly by Arthur Fletcher, a railway wagon contractor of Nottingham; the 'new specification' type by Central Wagon Co Ltd of Wigan and by Thos. Hunter Ltd of Rugby (per *Quarry Manager's Journal*, 5th August 1925, p.31). According to local sources, the stock was in poor shape after its four-year weathering and in many cases probably only the ironwork was worth salvaging. The fate of the narrow gauge system is not recorded but it almost certainly went purely for scrap. The standard gauge wagon stock seems rather large for the size of the system but possibly included stock from Heyford Ironworks.

Thirty years later there were plenty of remains to be seen, the only important casualty being the wooden bridge over the SMJ — 'Bridge No 2 destroyed by fire 26th September 1929' as recorded by the LMSR. The course of the narrow gauge tramways could still easily be traced for the most part, the shell of the locomotive shed was standing, and there were four brick bridges under lanes. The route of the standard gauge section was also there, though occupied by a stream, and there were brick piers of a bridge crossing the line. The quarry site southeast of Gayton village and west of the SMJ line, which was probably the oldest, was restored to agricultural use in the early 1960s but there are still a few remains. The bridge under the Gayton-Blisworth road has been filled in, but on the southwest side a bushy gullet extends a hundred yards or so, then a ploughed-up section, a further hundred yards of terminal face, and finally a gullet overgrown with trees and filled with water, stretching up to the boundary roadside hedge. Across the ploughed-up piece a tramway ran to a further area of quarrying, evidence of which can be seen in the fields up to the backs of the houses in the village. The 1883 6in. OS shows isolated track here and there but none in the gullet to the south, so the latter was probably abandoned first. The ground carries many chunks of stone in the soil. On the northeast side of the road the quarry area is almost fully under the plough, and the standard gauge

Gayton Quarries (Sparrow). Piers of former bridge over the connection to the LNWR Blisworth-Rugby line. This bridge carried the narrow gauge tramway from the pits, and the tubs emptied their loads via chutes into railway wagons. This site is now even more heavily overgrown. 6th April 1953 (G. H. Starmer)

Gayton Quarries (Sparrow). Bridge under the Blisworth-Gayton road, south side. 30th October 1982. (Eric Tonks)

trackbed is eroded by the stream and masked by impenetrable undergrowth for part of the way, though the connection at the BR end is still clearly defined. The pits east of the SMJ line still have something to show, commencing with a cutting along the north side of the Gayton-Blisworth road as far as the crossroads, where the bridge under the Tiffield road has been filled in; the other bridge on this road, 250 yards south of the crossroads, is still visible however, also the opening on the south side of the bridge under the Gayton-Blisworth road (the north side has been filled in). These bridges are of the simplest kind, of red brick without any embellishment and using existing stonework where possible. The quarrying area in the four sections round the crossroads is denoted by the fields now being well below road level, but there are no quarry faces left except the roadsides, in particular the eastern side of the Tiffield road. One interesting relic in George Freeston's collection is a twelve-inch long iron roller discovered about 1976 by John Huckerby of Gayton Wood on the site of the incline just above the SMJ route. This still has the long nails by which it was presumably nailed to a sleeper, with the object of keeping the cable clear of the ground; it seems however never to have been oiled—not latterly anyhow—as the steel cable has worn nearly half way through the roller in its fixed state.

Grid References

708543	Tippler
709542	Bridge over SMJR
707543	Bridge under Gayton-Blisworth road, E of SMJR
711539	Bridge under Gayton-Blisworth road, W of SMJR
712536	Bridge under Tiffield road
713539	Bridge under Tiffield road by cross roads
711544	Standard gauge locomotive shed
710540	Narrow gauge locomotive shed
715550	Connection to LNWR

Locomotives

Gauge; 2ft. 10in.

GAYTON	0-4-0ST OC	?			s/s c 1918
-	4 w P M	Groom & Tattersall, Towcester	c 1918	New	s/s

Gauge; 4ft. 8½in.

-	0-4-0ST OC FW	331	1877	12 x 18in.	3ft. 0½in.	New 1877	(1)

(1) to Monkton Main Coal Co Ltd, Yorkshire.

GAYTON QUARRIES

Owner: Henry W. Wheldon.

The Railway Clearing House maps of 1888 and 1901 show 'Wheldon's Siding' at a distance of 1 mile 20 chains from Blisworth SMJR station, and the 1883 6in. OS map shows a line running roughly northwest-southeast to the SMJR at this point, and isolated at the northwest end from the Gayton Wood tramway. This presumed narrow gauge line debouches onto the cutting of the SMJR where a brick occupation bridge crosses the line south of the Blisworth-Gayton road. In plan it seems quite feasible to transfer ore from the narrow gauge to main line, but a visit to the spot reveals that the cutting here is very deep (about 60ft.) and shovelling, for example, would have been out of the question. However, there was a recollection in the village that Wheldon 'fitted his carts with skids to allow them to slide down the hill-side to Gayton Sidings'. Putting these data together, one gets a picture of wagons with removable bodies that were put on skids and lowered down the steep slope to the siding and the ore shovelled or tipped out at the foot. It seems an extraordinary arrangement but the topography allows of no reasonable alternative; there is no trackway down the cutting side. An old resident living at Blisworth Arm told George Freeston that some ore was brought from Gayton in carts and loaded into canal boats; possibly this applied also to Wheldon's quarries.

Wheldon is recorded in MS as being in operation from 1863 to 1884, and the quarry as disused in 1885. 'Wheldon's Siding' still appears on the RCH map for 1901 but in 1909 is shown as 'Wheldon & Sparrow's Siding'. The SMJR Working Timetable for October 1912 simply shows 'Wheldon's Siding'.[1]

The quarry site is slightly hummocky but otherwise there is no trace of the line, and the railway banks are heavily overgrown now. However, on the side of the SMJ cutting, opposite to where the narrow gauge terminated, are a series of four posts up the bank; possibly they had some connection with the wagon transfer operation — but this is guesswork.

Footnote

1.   I am indebted to Mr. A. St. G. Walsh for the RCH and SMJ Working Timetable information that has helped so materially in unravelling this tangle. His letter of 29th January 1970 to the author refers.

Grid References

707537   Tipping point on SMJR

BLISWORTH QUARRIES

Owners: Richard Thomas & Co Ltd; Richard Thomas & Baldwins Ltd from 3rd January 1945

These quarries were a revival of the earlier Blisworth/Gayton quarries on a more comprehensive scale, in accordance with 20th century practice, instead of the piecemeal efforts of their predecessors. After World War I a large area (about 2000 acres) of land in the parishes of Blisworth, Gayton, Tiffield and Easton Neston was offered by Blisworth & Towcester Ironstone Estates Ltd to the iron ore industry, but in the difficult conditions of the time there were no takers. Richard Thomas & Co Ltd was one company which considered the offer, in the light of a favourable report dated 29th November 1921 by Henry Louis, Professor of Mining, but it was not until fourteen years later that they took up the matter. In September 1935 they acquired 1205 acres from Blisworth & Towcester Ironstone Estates Ltd, and a further 173 acres (Gayton Wood Farm) from the Hawley Estates Co: but even then no practical steps were taken until the outbreak of World War II, when the Ministry of Supply Home Ore Department commenced arrangements with Richard Thomas to 'reopen Blisworth Quarry', aiming at an output of 5000-6000 tons per week. Under an agreement dated 15th February 1940 the Treasury would take care of expenses incurred and at the end of hostilities the company would be given the option to purchase the plant and equipment, which was to include a Ruston Bucyrus 5W dragline and a Ransomes & Rapier 490 loading shovel.

Planning of the rail system caused almost as much difficulty as it had in the distant past, and the first proposal, shown on a plan dated 23rd August 1940, was for a tramway running southwest to northeast across the orefield, connecting with the former SMJR line due east of Gayton Wood Farm (or House, as it is shown on the OS) skirting the latter to the south then through Fox Covert and obliquely down the hillside to a wharf on the canal; perhaps Richard Thomas had plans to relight Hunsbury Furnaces, which they had then acquired—there seems no more likely explanation. This plan was however superseded by another, making a connection to the SMJ two thirds of a mile nearer Blisworth, then running for half its route along the west side of the Gayton-Blisworth parish boundary. This too was altered, the SMJR junction remaining the same but the line climbing the hill to pass beneath the Blisworth-Gayton and Gayton-Tiffield roads. This was in November 1940, when there came an unexpected delay; to lay the line required the sanction of the landowner, Sir David Hawley — and he was a prisoner of war in Germany. Sir Frederic Scopes of the Home Ore Control wrote somewhat wearily on 11th February 1941: '...the lawyers still seem to be wrangling about the land. I hope there will not be much more delay, I'm interested nowadays in output, not reports and documents!' After a four-month delay approval was received from the landowner, whose reply, countersigned by the Stalag Commandant, is preserved with the files at Corby; we wonder if the Commandant knew that the land was to be developed in order to provide munitions!

Things got moving in earnest in September 1941, negotiations for the main line connection were made with the LMSR and quarry machines and locomotives ordered; the initial plans of a year before provided for a diesel locomotive because of possible difficulties in getting water supplies, but this problem had evidently been overcome and a steam locomotive was chosen. The contractors building the system, Trevor Construction Co Ltd of Weybridge, used an Andrew Barclay locomotive on the work; according to the *Railway Observer* (1943, p.204), a Hardy petrol locomotive was also used. Work continued through the winter; it must be remembered that this was wartime and even for projects under direct Government jurisdiction licenses were essential for plant. The LMSR siding was officially opened 20th December 1941, as A. St. G. Walsh records. In the early summer E. D. Sharman & Son Ltd of Northampton built the locomotive shed and appurtenances and erected later a water tank near the crossroads. In May 1942 the Ministry of Supply Home Ore Department put forward a scheme to calcine the Blisworth output, estimated at 4000 tons per week, and when finally approved (January 1943) this involved the purchase of three machines (a 55RB crawler, 37RB shovel and 10RB grab), 24 skip wagons and a 16in. Andrew Barclay locomotive, requiring also a front-end extension to the locomotive shed; and twelve men to be diverted from the shoe industry. The aim of the scheme was to save transport costs on long-distance haulage, but Richard Thomas were not enthusiastic; they had purchased the land to provide ore for their own use in due time but under wartime pressures the site had been opened up to feed furnaces elsewhere. Some doubts about the suitability of Blisworth ore for calcining had been sounded at the start and were now raised again, the orders for plant being suspended meanwhile; new tests confirmed these misgivings and the scheme was finally abandoned on 31st May 1943.

These events did not affect production of raw ironstone, however, which was put in hand soon after the arrival in August 1942 of the two quarry machines (a 5W walking dragline and a 49O shovel) and the locomotive; output commenced with the despatch on 30th November 1942 of a load to

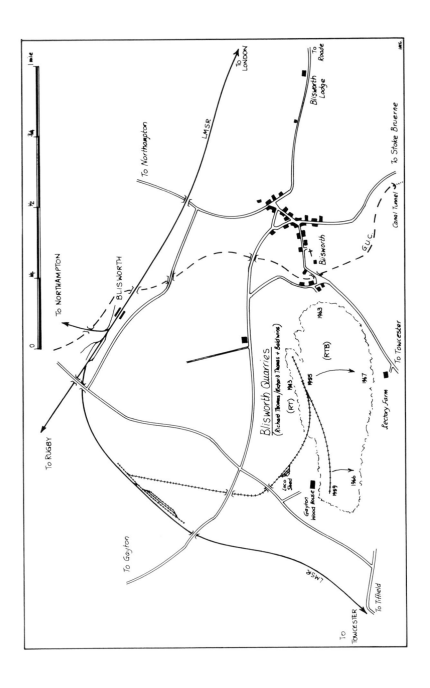

Skinningrove ironworks and continued at the rate of about 2000 tons per week, nearly all to Skinningrove or Consett ironworks; by June 1943 output had dropped to 1000 tons per week and the decision of Consett to cancel their orders at the beginning of October led to the closure of the quarries. This was formally confirmed by the MOS Home Ore Department on 12th November 1943 but it was stipulated that the rail tracks and fixed plant be left in position for six years after the termination of the agreement with the MOS. The ore quarried was east north east of the locomotive shed area.

The rail link started at a junction with the former SMJ line, where reception sidings were provided and a gate across the track indicated the change of ownership. The first and steeply graded section ran obliquely across the course of Sparrow's old line and at the summit of the bank was partly in cutting to pass beneath the Blisworth-Gayton road and then turned sharply east, but where it emerged from the tunnel under the Gayton-Tiffield road it was at the level of the fields, which were some 10ft. below that of the neighbouring lanes as a result of the earlier excavations; here were situated the locomotive shed, weighbridge and a fitting shop for wagon repairs etc, and access to the premises was attained by means of a wooden ladder from a stile—a curious and possibly unique rural sight. Beyond the buildings the line ran slightly downhill to the quarry, with a passing loop near the entrance. Spiked 40ft. rails on concrete or wooden sleepers were used and the ballasting was of an excellence rarely seen other than on a main line railway, such that weeds made little headway after nine years of dereliction. The tunnels were of reinforced concrete. The quarry machines were of the makers' standard patterns and the locomotive was a standard 14in. Andrew Barclay, which according to the order was to be painted 'green and red, lined yellow, and with *BLISWORTH NO. 1* on the saddle tank'.

As we have seen, the quarry had a working life of just under twelve months, for most of which the output was less than half the expected figure of 5000-6000 tons per week, hardly justifying the heavy outlay. According to a summary published in 1965,[1] the Blisworth quarry was a 'War Measure hurriedly conceived as a short term policy. The fear of shortage of Iron Ore did not materialise and the development was stopped and the plant disposed of'. A final inspection on behalf of the Ministry of Supply was made at the beginning of March 1944 and the movable equipment transferred to more productive work elsewhere; the 490 shovel went to Frodingham ironstone quarries and the 5W to Colsterworth quarries. The locomotive was used on the dismantling operations and then remained idle in its shed until September 1944; Oxfordshire Ironstone Co Ltd

Blisworth Quarries (RTB). The quarries were reopened as a wartime emergency measure under the auspices of the Ministry of Supply, but were only in production for twelve months, when the system was 'mothballed' until 1954. The photograph shows (left to right) the well-built weigh office, locomotive shed and fitting shop. April 1953. (G. H. Starmer)

expressed a wish to have her, but a drop in their output removed the need and she went to Storefield quarries instead. The rest of the equipment, including large quantities of spares, was left intact apart from hurdles placed across the line to prevent cattle straying, so that reopening would be a very simple matter should demand warrant it. Since the line was designed so that standard wagons could be taken directly to the working face, none were left on the system save a flat wagon of the type used by platelayers, and housed in the shed.

The agreement with the MOS terminated on 15th February 1946, when in accordance with the terms of the closure the land and buildings were left as

Blisworth Quarries (RTB). View taken in 1954 from the boom of the 5360 stripping shovel, then in course of erection, with Blisworth village in the background. The quarry shown is the one worked in World War II. (George Freeston)

Blisworth Quarries (RTB), General view from the Gayton road, showing the 5360 in course of building. The sunken fields in the foreground were quarried by earlier operators. Note the 'wall' and hedge in the centre, which is the parish boundary between Blisworth and Gayton. Phipps worked ground to the left, R. B. Sparrow to the right. c 1954.

(George Freeston)

Blisworth Quarries (RTB). *BLISWORTH No. 1* (the second locomotive to bear this name) outside the weigh office 1st September 1955. Production started just one week later. (George Freeston)

Blisworth Quarries (RTB). Jib of the 5360 being taken up to the quarry by *BLISWORTH No. 1* from the shed yard. The concrete bridge is that under the Tiffield road, and at the left is the old brick bridge used by R. B. Sparrow, for the narrow gauge tramway. 1955. (A. J. Pack)

they were; but it was not until 1952 that Richard Thomas & Baldwins Ltd considered the possibility of reopening. In the early Spring of 1953 drilling for samples in the Glebe Farm area was made and in June 1953 it was decided to reopen Blisworth in connection with the new blast furnace programme at Scunthorpe, for which an increased output of ore would be required in 1955. There was some discussion as to whether the existing system should be extended, working opencast, or whether to introduce mining, using a narrow gauge tramway system as at Irthlingborough. It was decided to reopen the original short face and work opencast, using the 5360 Ransomes & Rapier shovel that had been lying disused at Finedon since the quarries there closed in 1946, and a new *BLISWORTH No. 1* was ordered from Andrew Barclay's. Before it was delivered, a Peckett *HENRY CORT* was brought up from Ebbw Vale, early in 1954; the hurdles were removed and the engine was used to bring up from the BR line materials required for the reopening, chiefly parts of the 680-ton excavator from Finedon; this job done, she retired to the shed until the erection of the excavator could be completed. The southern end of the locomotive shed was knocked out and an extension built to the same pattern as the existing building (probably by the same firm) to accommodate *BLISWORTH No. 1* which arrived early in 1955 and, the navvy still not being ready, was greased up and put into store until required for production later in the year. Though dimensionally similar to the previous bearer of the name, the new locomotive incorporated some new features, including a slightly deeper tank and a modified cab with rounded angles to the roof; the works plates were smaller and of cast iron instead of brass; the painting style was similar to that of the earlier locomotive, consisting of light Brunswick green with yellow lining, the lettering as before being gold with red shading.

A further locomotive, *ETTRICK*, was obtained in 1957 from Abelsons, the plant dealers, and bore a small brass plate on the cabside 'Abelson & Co (Engineers) Ltd Owners LA 248.'; this referred to the time *ETTRICK* was hired out by Abelsons on contract work, but was not removed when the locomotive was sold. She displaced *HENRY CORT* and with the new *BLISWORTH No. 1* worked the traffic unaided for five years; both were in steam daily, one working between quarry and weighbridge and the other between weighbridge and the BR line. There was no spare locomotive, and it was evident that the lavish expenditure typified by the equipping of the line in the first place was not to be perpetuated. Subsequent locomotive acquisitions were both secondhand and rumour of the purchase of a 200-horsepower Sentinel steam locomotive in 1954 proved unfounded. The two fresh locomotives comprised a six-wheeled Hunslet displaced from

Ebbw Vale steelworks by dieselization, and *SIEMENS* from Irthlingborough mines after the latter had closed down. This last was the more interesting in that she was one of the comparatively rare 'home-made' locomotives and carried plates *'Ebbw Vale Steel Coal & Iron Co Ltd, Ebbw Vale Works. Makers 1909. No. 25'*; however, she looked very much like a typical Peckett and was almost certainly constructed at Ebbw Vale from parts supplied by Pecketts. Ebbw Vale had a large fleet of Peckett locomotives.

The livery of *BLISWORTH No. 1* (both of them) has been mentioned, and the other locomotives were all green, some with various embellishments. *49* had red rods and on the cabside a brass plate carrying the number on a red background, and *'No. 49'* painted in yellow on the tank; the footplate and rear carried black and yellow dazzle stripes. *SIEMENS* was also green with a dazzle smokebox front of yellow and black, and a dazzle panel of green and black beneath the boiler. *ETTRICK* arrived painted light green, with red rods and chromium-plated nameplates; but in 1967 she appeared in an extraordinary livery of duck-egg blue, with alternate letters of the right-hand nameplate painted red — perhaps the driver's idiosyncracy.

Production began with 208 tons despatched on 1st September 1955. The railway layout was a simple one, though initially involving a reversal into

Blisworth Quarries (RTB). *HENRY CORT* in June 1957; she was moved to Irthlingborough a month later. Her chimney was damaged by an excavator. (S. A. Leleux)

Blisworth Quarries (RTB). Hunslet locomotive at the BR sidings on 15th June 1965, with the brakevan and train. The dumpcar at the right was in use as a coal store.   (S. A. Leleux)

the quarry; the working face lengthened as operations proceeded clockwise, eventually stretching almost from the Tiffield road southwest of Gayton Wood House to near the A43 Towcester road a quarter mile northeast of Rectory Farm. The final face was over three quarters of a mile in length and the last cuts were made at the Towcester road end, so that reversals were then unnecessary. More important was the steep rise from the shed area to the second bridge, then the much longer descent to the BR line. A few runaways occurred in the early stages of operation of the reopened line, and as a result a former Midland Railway 20-ton brakevan was obtained from BR for extra braking power. The locomotive was at the

Blisworth Quarries (RTB). Concrete bridge under the Blisworth-Gayton road. Notice says 'Set brakes before restarting'. c 1965.   (A. J. Pack)

downhill end (all locomotives faced uphill) with the brakevan coupled to it, and the normal train was four loaded tipplers; between quarry and locomotive shed two only was usual. A notice to this effect 'Four wagons only' stood beside the track by the first bridge. Brakes were pinned down at the second road bridge, where there was a notice with this instruction, and near the junction with the BR sidings was a notice 'Check your brakes again'. The shunter rode in the van, to apply the second brake during the descent. It was because of these somewhat complicated manoeuvres that it was necessary to have two locomotives in steam, one working the bank and one working between shed and quarry, as otherwise the four wagons at the pitface would be filled long before the locomotive's return. Coming up the bank, eight empties were permitted, hence on the last trip of the day the locomotive and brakevan ascended light. Because of her six wheels, *49* was regarded as better on the bank, but was not so happy on the sharp curve at the top; she was withdrawn in 1966, leaving the four-wheelers to do the work. Catch points were placed between the two bridges to prevent runaway wagons entering the yard.

When the BR (former SMJ) line was closed as a through route, the track was lifted just beyond the RTB sidings and the usual method then was for the BR class 08 diesel shunter to push the empties up from Blisworth station, these empties being left on the old SMJ running line; the diesel would then take the full wagons from the sidings, 14 at a time, to Blisworth and then push the empties into the exchange sidings, a task that the RTB locomotive was not allowed to perform. At weekends and when the railway was not in use generally, hurdles were placed over the track by the bridge near the shed to prevent cattle straying; at holiday times even barbed wire was used.

Wagons were usually standard BR 27-ton tipplers, and there were two flat wagons used for conveying excavating equipment when necessary, a common feature of ironstone quarry railways. There were also a number of 'dumpcars', commonly associated with calcining operations, and consisting of a steel body mounted such that the load could be side-tipped on a calcine bank. As the output from Blisworth went to RTB's works at Scunthorpe and Port Talbot, both lengthy hauls, calcining would seem to have been worthwhile and was evidently intended, but so far as we are aware, no calcining was done, and the only recollections of these vehicles is of seeing a string of them on an isolated length of track between shed and quarry, and one at the BR headshunt used as a coal store.

There were three quarry machines, the first being the Ransomes & Rapier 5360 type electric shovel that was assembled on site in 1954/5, with the

Blisworth Quarries (RTB). The BR sidings on the former SMJ line, by this time reduced to a spur from Blisworth station to this point. *SIEMENS* plus attendant brakevan shunts. The line to the quarries is by the fence in the foreground. 30th August 1967.　　　　(M. J. Leah)

Blisworth Quarries (RTB). *SIEMENS* pulls and *ETTRICK* pushes a train of four loaded wagons towards the weighbridge in front of the bridge under the Tiffield road, 29th March 1967.　　　　(G. H. Starmer)

Blisworth Quarries (RTB). Grafton steam crane used for odd jobs about the quarry in the reopening stages. 1956. (George Freeston)

assistance of a Grafton vertical-boilered steam crane; the 5360s were always impressive machines and this one dominated the skyline over Blisworth High Street. For loading, a 490 Ransomes & Rapier electric shovel was used, but not the one that had served here in the earlier phase of activity. The last machine was a Ransomes & Rapier W90 diesel-electric walking

Blisworth Quarries (RTB). Wet conditions were frequently encountered in the quarry, as on this winter's day, with the machines mirrored in the puddles. At the rear 5360 removed overburden, while the 490 in the foreground loads wagons in the charge of *BLISWORTH No. 1.* 31st December 1966. (G. H. Starmer)

Blisworth Quarries (RTB). The quarries in action with the W90 and 490 machines. c.1965.

(A. J. Pack)

dragline to deal with the heavier overburden.

The middle 1960s was a period of reduced demand for ironstone by the industry and this, coupled with the rising freight charges by BR, led to the closure of several of the smaller quarries. Blisworth was particularly badly placed geographically, as its ore was sent to Scunthorpe or South Wales, both considerable distances, and in 1967 output had fallen to a mere 1500 tons per week, about 55 wagon loads; the Blisworth pits were capable of producing 8000 tons per week and at this time the ore was of a high quality. The weekly freight bill amounted to around £5000. A fitter in 1967 reported that the place was being 'run on a shoestring'. The decision to close therefore came as no great surprise and took place on 30th September 1967; as usual, 'obituaries' appeared in the local press. Buckminster was to supply ore to RTB's works at Scunthorpe.

Dismantling of the track commenced immediately at the far end of the quarry, working back towards the main line. Both rail and road vehicles were used, *BLISWORTH No. 1* and two flat trolleys being used to convey lifted rail down to the branch; road vehicles were employed to remove stores in the shed area. In January 1968 the cutting was flooded, slowing down the work somewhat, but this was not a new phenomenon; production had been maintained even when the quarry floor was two feet deep in water! *49* and *SIEMENS* were cut up in the spring, the plates of the former being retained by RTB, while the works plates of *SIEMENS* went into storage. *ETTRICK* was retained and kept in the shed with the brakevan. However in June 1968 they were moved outside and the connecting line to the shed was severed; by this time all the line down to the BR sidings had been removed. The two remaining locomotives then stood on a section of track outside the shed.

Blisworth Quarries (RTB). *ETTRICK*, in her livery of duck-egg blue, emerges from the quarry with two loaded wagons, 30th August 1967, Note the derelict dumpcars in the foreground, presumably purchased for a calcining operation which was not put into effect.
(M. J. Leah)

Blisworth Quarries (RTB). *HENRY CORT* ascending the incline to the Gayton road bridge on 20th September 1958. The depth of the cutting was accentuated here by the piles of excavated earth on each side. On restoration, this was returned to the cutting.
(G. H. Starmer)

Meanwhile the dragline was busy levelling the quarry area for restoration to agriculture; the 5360 shovel was dismantled for transit to Buckminster, to work the new quarries at Stainby Warren that were to supply Scunthorpe. 1969 saw the virtual completion of the process of levelling and filling, and by the end of the year only a section of the final gullet and the area in the vicinity of the shed retained any resemblance of the working quarry railway. The formation north of the bridge under the Blisworth-Gayton road had been incorporated into the surrounding fields, the cutting being filled in from the spoil heaps that had lain alongside since the line was opened. Similarly, the area beyond the shed had been levelled and indeed some was already under cultivation. However, the locomotive shed and associated buildings were there, as was *BLISWORTH No. 1* and both the concrete bridges. These solidly built structures were left in for access to the fields, and a visit to the spot will soon show why. Ground in the vicinity of the nearby crossroads was quarried extensively in the late 19th and early 20th centuries, and the level of the fields was reduced by some 12 to 15ft. below that of the lanes; when quarrying was resumed further to the east it was only possible to approach 'ground level' from some distance away from the crossroads (or by the ladder in the hedge by the shed). When quarrying ceased again, access was still difficult — hence the retention of the two bridges.

ETTRICK was purchased for preservation by the Burton Historical Transport Museum and left Blisworth in April 1969 (between the 13th and 27th); she was stored for the museum people at the Ministry of Defence Sudbury depot, and then seems to have disappeared from mortal ken. A Mr.

Blisworth Quarries (RTB). *ETTRICK* and *BLISWORTH No. 1* on a short length of track in April 1969. Compare with 1953 photo. (G. Warner)

Nicholson of Draycott-in-the-Clay acquired her, but later on sold her to another man on the understanding that she was to be preserved; however, the buyer was a scrap merchant who promptly cut up *ETTRICK*. To *BLISWORTH No. 1* goes a singular and melancholy distinction; to the best of our knowledge she was the very last British steam industrial locomotive to be sold from one industry to another other than for scrap. On 29th May 1970 a Pickfords lowloader carted her away to Goldington power station; in the event, she was never steamed there but very possibly provided spares for their other Barclays of similar design.

The dragline remained in the quarry long after finishing its task of restoration, but disappeared in the first half of 1976, probably being dismantled on site and the pieces taken away for scrap. One other item remains to be mentioned; in 1965 Geoffrey Starmer noted close to the BR sidings a narrow gauge tub buried up to the rim and apparently used as a cattle trough—though by then obscured by brambles. It was a typical V-shaped steel side-tipper that may have had its origin in the quarries—though this seems unlikely by the design.

The present day situation will be generally apparent from what has been said already—the concrete bridges under roads: the buildings, now owned by a farmer, grouped round the former shed yard and comprising the

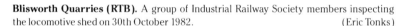

Blisworth Quarries (RTB). A group of Industrial Railway Society members inspecting the locomotive shed on 30th October 1982. (Eric Tonks)

locomotive shed, workshops, weighbridge and iron water tank, all looking rather incongruous in open green fields: and a larger water tank near the crossroads. The whole quarry area has been graded suitably and much of it is under the plough, with wire fences or new hedges flanked by wire, replacing the originals. Looking east from the locomotive shed, it is hard to believe that a railway once penetrated these fields. The inclined section down to BR has left a vague depression but the iron tub body mentioned was still present in 1979, lying on the ballast; a typical V-shaped skip 44in. long, 47in. wide and 24in. deep—unfortuntately not very likely to have had any direct association with the quarries.

Enthusiasts inspecting the locomotive shed will notice a small building tacked on to the side, rather like a dog-kennel, and obviously of much later construction than the main building, and with a piece of 3ft. gauge track embedded in its concrete floor. Enquiry locally and among RTB personnel has entirely failed to discover the purpose of this structure; it is shown on an RTB drawing in the files, with no descriptive comment. The track was possibly for reinforcement only. It is indeed odd, as it was only built just as the place was due for closure.

There is in the vicinity one quarry, which can be reached by a trackway near Rectory Farm on the Towcester road; it has however no connection with RTB and was opened up as a source of limestone by a firm of contractors (Dowsett Minerals Recovery Ltd—a subsidiary of RTB) engaged in the building of the M1 motorway. Unlike the ironstone quarries, this was not restored and has been sold to S. W. Wreford & Sons Ltd, the haulage contractors of Northampton; it has been designated a nature reserve and some deciduous trees have been planted in it. The limestone face is still clearly visible. A little to the east, downhill, stood the excavators, and the approach road to these, on the east side of Rectory Farm, is now used by tenants for access.

Footnote

1.   *Steel & Coal; a Technical Survey of the Richard Thomas & Baldwin Group,* I am indebted to Trevor Lodge for this item.

Grid References

713545	BR connection
712539	Bridge under Blisworth-Gayton road
712537	Bridge under Tiffield road
713536	Locomotive shed

Blisworth Quarries (RTB). Ironstone was quarried from this site for over a century, but it can hardly be said to have defaced the countryside to any great extent. Indeed, quarrying added something that has now been lost. Our picture shows *SIEMENS* pushing a train of empties up from the BR sidings on 30th August 1967. (M. J. Leah)

Locomotives

First Period (1941-45)
Gauge; 4ft. 8½in.

BLISWORTH No. 1   0-4-0ST OC AB 2143   1942 14 x 22in.   3ft. 5in.   New 8/1942 (1)

(1) to South Durham Steel & Iron Co Ltd, Storefield Quarries, 9/1944

Second Period (1954-69)
Gauge; 4ft. 8½in.

HENRY CORT	0-4-0ST	OC	P	933	1903	14 x 20in.	3ft. 2in.		(a)	(1)
					Reb. Ebbw Vale 1920, 1937					
BLISWORTH No. 1	0-4-0ST	OC	AB	2365	1955	14 x 22in.	3ft. 5in.	New 2/1955		(2)
ETTRICK	0-4-0ST	OC	HL	3721	1928	14 x 22in.	3ft. 6in.		(b)	(3)
49	0-6-0ST	IC	HE	2082	1940	16 x 22in.	3ft. 9in.		(c)	Scr 3/1968
SIEMENS	0-4-0ST	OC	EV	3	1909				(d)	Scr 3-4/1968

(a) ex Ebbw Vale Steel Coal & Iron Co Ltd, Ebbw Vale Steelworks, 1954.
(b) ex Abelson & Co (Engineers) Ltd, Sheldon, Birmingham, 5/1957.
(c) ex Ebbw Vale Steelworks, 9/1962.
(d) ex Irthlingborough Mines, 4/1966.

(1) to Irthlingborough Mines, 7/1957.
(2) to CEGB Goldington Power Station, Bedfordshire, 5/1970.
(3) to store at MOD Marchington, Staffordshire, for Burton Historical Transport Museum, 4/1969.

Quarry Machines

First Period (1941-45)

490	E. Shovel	R&R	1304	1942	2½ Cu.Yd.	28ft. 6in.	New 8/1942	(1)
5W	E. Dragline	RB	6305	1942	3½ Cu.Yd.	35ft.	New 8/1942	(2)

(1) to Frodingham Ironstone Mines Ltd 3/1944
(2) to Colsterworth Quarries 4/1944

Second Period (1954-69)

5360	E. Shovel	R&R	669	1937	9 Cu.Yd.	104ft.	(a)	(1)
490	D. Shovel. Caterpillar	R&R	1256	1941	2½ Cu.Yd.	36ft.	(a)	s/s
W90	E. Walking Dragline	R&R	2055	1945	2 Cu.Yd.	114ft.	(b)	Scr 1976

(a) ex Finedon Quarries c 1954.
(b) ex Sir Robert MacAlpine & Sons Ltd.

(1) to Buckminster Quarries c 1968.

SHOWSLEY (SEWARDSLEY) QUARRIES

Owners: Towcester Mineral & Brick Co Ltd

These were very shallow opencast pits served by a narrow gauge tramway along which tubs were pulled by horses (of which there were two) and their contents tipped into wagons on a standard gauge siding from the Stratford-upon-Avon, Towcester & Midland Junction Railway. Sewardsley is an old spelling that appears on maps but is not used locally.

There was a quarry on this site by the time of the promulgation of the Easton Neston, Towcester, Roade & Olney Junction Railway, and it is shown on the Deposited Plans of November 1878 for this railway; but whether this was for ore or for building stone is unknown. If the former, it could be an alternative site for the 'Shutlanger' quarries. The railway was originally planned to pass through the quarry area, but the route was revised to run to the south. The first written record of Showsley pits is for 1909; the owners applied on 29th June 1909 to the SMJ for a siding to be put in, and

Showsley Quarries. The ironstone face at Round Plantation, looking towards the road, 9th January 1979. Further quarrying here was prohibited by the landowner. (Eric Tonks)

this was opened for traffic 27th September 1909. According to Mr. Warren, the only former employee who has been located, the quarries were closed about 1913, but the SMJ traffic manager reported to his board on 13th June 1918 that the ironstone was worked out and the siding closed, which suggests a closure nearer 1918.

The system was only a small one, and permission to cut down trees in Adams Grove (or The Round Plantation) to remove the ore beneath was refused, so the tramway had to skirt round it. By 1967 the pasture had been ploughed and crops sown, obliterating traces on the ground except for a broad depression from the SMJ trackbed towards Round Plantation, on the south and east sides of which the ironstone face is very well preserved, and the terminal point well marked. The situation was unchanged in 1979.

Grid Reference

720504   Face at Round Plantation

Grid Reference

725502   Quarry

SHUTLANGER QUARRIES

Owners: Towcester Iron Ore Co.

These quarries are recorded in MS for 1873/4, i.e. before the railway arrived; the Towcester to Olney Junction line was opened 18th April 1891. According to information given by an old resident to Mr. L. V. Bootman, the pits were at Huddiemoor, about half way between Shutlanger village and the Round Plantation; the output was presumably taken away by cart, probably to Towcester via the line from Easton Neston. A small pit is shown on the 1900 OS, and a small area of lower-level ground is evident today, on each side of the nearby fence at this site. Another possibility is that the Shutlanger quarries were by the Round Plantation, which were reopened in 1909 as Showsley Quarries (which see page 60).

EASTON NESTON QUARRIES

Owners: Towcester Iron Ore Co: Easton Estates & Mining Co Ltd from 1878: Towcester Mineral & Brick Co Ltd from 14th November 1889: Richard J. Harry from 1903: E. M. Jellett from 1918 (Towcester Mineral & Brick Co Ltd title also used throughout); Blisworth & Towcester Ironstone Estates Ltd from c.1920.

Easton Neston quarries were operated for nearly half a century although throughout their existence they seem to have been commercially precarious, epitomized by breaks in production and changes in management; but, while they were never extensive, their rail transport system was particularly interesting. According to MS, production began in 1873, the early development of the quarries being tied up with the erection of Towcester Furnaces, put in blast in 1875; these were close to the east side of the Northampton & Banbury Junction Railway, one mile north of Towcester, and consisted of two rotary furnaces that were pioneers of Dr. C. W. Siemen's 'Direct Process' of steel manufacture in contra-distinction to the prevailing use of the Bessemer process. Linked with this development was none other than Samuel Lloyd, later to be responsible for the start of the great Corby empire; his involvement is described in his *Reminiscences* (published privately in 1913), in which he credits his Cornish mining agent with bringing to his notice 'a most valuable mine in Towcester'. *Reminiscences* is weak on dates, and makes no mention of the ironworks but a brief report in the *Northampton Mercury* of 8th March 1873 refers to him in this capacity — he was a director of Towcester Iron Co Ltd — and the railway connection was called 'Lloyd's Siding', indicating his involvement from the start.

Samuel Lloyd obtained a lease from Sir Thomas Hesketh of Easton Neston Hall for working ironstone, and as there was also a thick bed of clay on the property, the manufacture of bricks was undertaken, for a 'brisk trade to the north of London'. The area of the lease is not stated, but it lay on both sides of the Northampton-Towcester road, north of Easton Neston Park. At this time, the railway from Towcester to Ravenstonewood Junction had not been built, and a standard gauge line just over a mile in length was built from the furnaces to a point east of the road which it crossed on the level; the 1883 6in. OS shows this line to have been laid almost to main line standards, with cuttings, and a signal guarding access to Towcester. The brickworks was erected west of the Northampton-Towcester road and an ironstone quarry was opened on the east side, with a narrow gauge

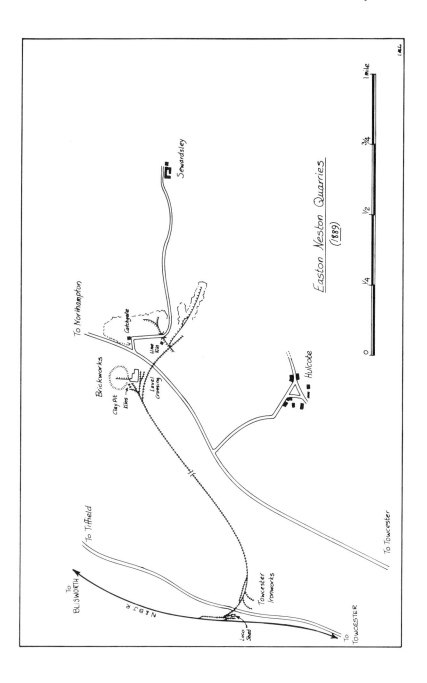

Easton Neston Quarries
(1889)

tramway to convey the ore to a tipping dock over the standard gauge line near its terminus. Quarrying seems to have started alongside the main road and moved eastwards, on both sides of the minor road to Showsley at Catchgate, with the cover increasing, and the 1883 6in. OS shows the tramway passing under this minor road; there were stables for the horses on the west side of the bridge. Quarrying for outcrop stone also took place in fields to the east, to which two branch tramways were laid. Traffic on the standard gauge line was presumably worked by the ironworks locomotive.

Samuel Lloyd says 'For a time this property seemed a very promising one until we reached a fault, abruptly cutting off the ironstone'. No date given, of course, but possibly 1878, when the Easton Estates & Mining Co Ltd took over; this company acquired the furnaces also in 1881 but both quarry and works were closed in 1882; *Mining Journal* for 3rd February 1883 states 'Towcester Furnaces have been out of blast for some considerable time, as the quality of the ore is unsuitable for the Direct Process'. The brickworks was taken over in 1889 by a new company under the style of Towcester Mineral & Brick Co Ltd, and a certain amount of iron ore was obtained from the quarries alongside. The new company introduced a locomotive for shunting but by this time the Towcester-Ravenstonewood Junction line was open (it was opened for traffic 18th April 1891) and a connection to it put in at Easton Neston, crossing the road on the level still; the former line from the brickworks to Towcester was then lifted.

The new venture did not flourish for very long and MS for 1901 describes the quarries as 'standing', with the company in liquidation the following year. The brickworks was closed down and the locomotive sold, being advertised for sale in the *Manchester Guardian* of 6th November 1902. However, in 1903 MS records that the quarries were once again in production under the ownership or management of Richard J. Harry; this gentleman had signed the documents required by H. M. Inspector of Quarries on behalf of the Towcester Mineral & Brick Co Ltd on 28th November 1896, and at that time was presumably the manager. Harry was drowned in the flooded brickpit in 1908, but his widow Alice and her brother, a Mr. Gardner (or Gardiner) carried on the business, and the old company name reappears in the records from 1908 onwards. There was a short break in production in 1918, but, as recorded by the SMJR at its board meeting of 13th June 1918 'the iron ore at Towcester Ironstone Sidings has been transferred from Mrs. Alice Harry to Mr. E. M. Jellett, who hopes to send out fifty wagons of ironstone per day'. The name E. M. Jellett is also quoted in *Rylands Directory* and in LQ; on the other hand, the Bagnall locomotive delivered in 1919 was ordered by the Towcester Mineral & Brick Co Ltd. Possibly Jellett had acquired the company. Incidentally, the SMJR line was locally referred to as 'The Bread & Herring', an interesting comparison with the 'Bread & Onion' applied to the LNWR line serving Islip Ironworks, presumably with reference to the limited diet of the navvies engaged in the constructional work.

Where quarrying was carried on during the first decade of the new century is not clear, and with the vicissitudes of ownership production was probably limited. Working is most likely to have taken place near the brickworks, on the northeast side, at the beginning of what was to become the most important quarry. About 1912 operations were recommenced at Catchgate (where the worked-out area had been planted with trees), working eastwards from the previous face; a small limekiln was also erected. To serve these workings a new tramway of 2ft. 6in. gauge was laid down; this was not carried over the SMJ siding, but ran parallel to it, with an extension to calcine banks and a reversing line to a tipping dock alongside the SMJR siding. Wagons were mostly U-shaped side-tippers, small ones holding about 1½ tons for the calcine bank, and some larger ones holding 3½ tons, the latter being of wood.

Easton Neston Quarries. *FERRET II.* Bagnall 1853. Though cut down in height, there was no requirement for this on the site. (Collection George Freeston)

Horses were used here at first but at the end of 1914 a secondhand Bagnall locomotive was acquired; this was *FERRET II*, built to negotiate a small bore tunnel, and had a maximum height of 6ft. 1in. from rail level to top of chimney, and a width of 5ft. 6in. As built she had an overall cab, but a photograph of her working at Easton Neston shows that the rear portion of the cab had been removed, and she probably arrived in this condition; later the TM&B blacksmith built a cab for her, and there was also an extension on the left hand side of the smokebox. Whether she was bought because of the restrictions imposed by the Catchgate tunnel or whether she just happened to be available is not certain. The presentday dimensions of the tunnel are 6ft. 5in. from roof to ground and 8ft. 1in. wide—a fairly tight squeeze vertically even for the aptly-named *FERRET II*—but the ground may have been lower then. 'Sergeant' Denny told Len Bootman that as a boy he remembered rakes of loaded wagons being run out of Catchgate by gravity, with a man on one to apply the brake as required; he is not certain if the locomotive was ever used, but it seems unlikely. The Catchgate pit was not worked very much, by 1920 being covered by Catchgate Plantation.[1] More important was the long east-west quarry west of the main road and north of the claypit, where by 1914 up to 35ft. of overburden had to be dealt with, for which a 12-ton Ruston steam navvy and transporter were purchased, the ore still being removed by hand.

The narrow gauge line was extended to cross the main road on the level close to the Showsley turn, and on the west side there was a trailing branch to the ironstone quarry. At the southern terminus was a square building containing office, stores, forge and workshops, and nearby were a corrugated iron locomotive shed and a water tank. With the brickworks closed and the ironstone quarry connected by a narrow gauge tramway to the exchange point, the SMJ line crossing the road was no longer required, and the opportunity seems to have been taken to realign the siding, slightly to the north of the old line and on a slightly higher level. The quarry west of the road was known as the Russia Pit, that on the east (Catchgate) became Canada Pit, though the origin of these odd names is unknown. Operating methods differed in the two pits to suit the conditions. In 'Canada' after the overburden had been removed ('unbaring') the ore would be loosened by pick but a solid pillar was left in; then the pillar would be knocked out, with a lookout man on top to warn those below when the whole section started to crack. In the much deeper 'Russia' pit the ironstone was first loosened by explosives, then loaded into tubs by hand; the men worked in pairs, and each pair was expected to load nine trucks per day, some sixteen men being employed thus. The loaded wagons were hauled

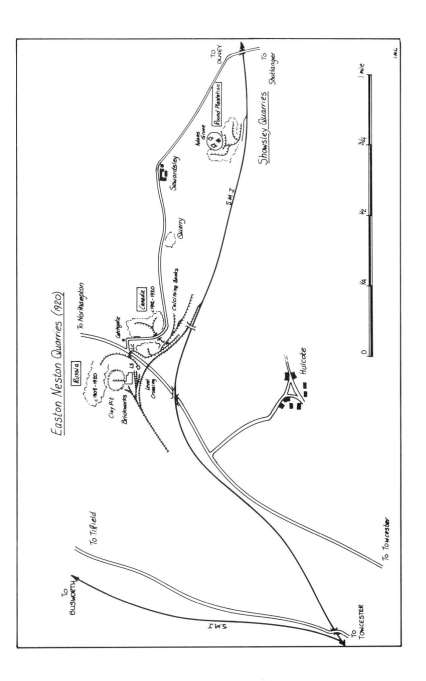

Easton Neston Quarries (1920)

Easton Neston Quarries. Tramway bridge under lane, with Catchgate Plantation beyond. The tramway was presumably lower when working; at this level even *FERRET II* would not get through, though so far as is known she never worked this pit. 2nd May 1984.(Eric Tonks)

Easton Neston Quarries. Ruston navvy and transporter in 'Russia' pit. Note narrow gauge line in pit bottom. c 1918. (Ruston & Hornsby)

out of the pit by locomotive, over the points, then pushed across the road and up the calcine bank. Water was a great problem, necessitating continuous pumping. We are fortunate in having so much detail about these quarries, about which so few documents survive. George Freeston obtained information from Bill Warren (clerk in the foreman's office) and Albert Goodridge, who started as 'Rope Boy' (the local equivalent to 'Rope-runner') and later worked on the transporter and both locomotives; and Len Bootman, who spent his childhood in one of the cottages built on the site of the earliest pits, has been tireless in collecting information on these quarries from old employees and local people.

The quarries were busy during World War I, and after the war extensions were evidently planned, with advertisements appearing in *The Engineer* (as Towcester Iron Stone Co) and *Machinery Market* (as Towcester Ironstone Co Ltd), both on 9th May 1919 for a '7in. or 8in.' locomotive of 2ft. 6in. gauge. However, no such locomotive seems to have been offered, and another Bagnall was purchased, named *RYDER GIBSON*, the original of which title is not as obvious as *FERRET*. The 1919 advertisement did not specify a cut-down locomotive, and while *RYDER GIBSON* had a low cab and a 'stubby' chimney (as described by Len Bootman) she did not have a dropped frame at the rear end. She worked exclusively in Russia Pit. Mr. C. R. H. Simpson, who lived in Towcester at the time, recollects her arrival at Towcester station, and he thought there was a 0-4-OT locomotive on the narrow gauge line at the quarry. However, the several members of the workforce interviewed by Len Bootman have failed to substantiate this. GSM states that mining was contemplated at one time, but this was never put into effect. The main Catchgate gullet was deeper than the earlier ones, to reach ore under greater cover, and was evidently not developed very far; in the Russia Pit working was easterly, with an extension northwards.

The quarries suffered from the postwar depression in the iron ore industry, and were closed in 1920. The Geological Association visited the site in May 1920, and the caption to a photograph refers to the 'ironstone for which the pit was worked' implying that work had ceased by then. The whole area, along with parts of Tiffield, Blisworth and Gayton, was put on the market by Blisworth & Towcester Ironstone Estates Ltd, but no buyers came forward until 1935, when Richard Thomas & Co Ltd took over the Blisworth and Gayton area. Arthur Travell of Shutlanger was retained as watchman, weeding the track and looking after the machinery. In 1925 *FERRET II* was sold to Blackwell's of Northampton and removed by road, and in 1928 it was decided to dismantle the system. *RYDER GIBSON* was put into steam to take tubs, track etc to the roadside for loading on to lorries, the level crossing having been removed during road repairs; the loco was sold to Thos W. Ward Ltd and taken away by rail, it is said. The material in Catchgate (which included trestles and planks from 'plank and barrow' working) was sent away by railway and the weighbridge was dismantled, but there was no restoration of the site on either side of the road. As a result, in spite of the changes that have taken place from time to time, there is still plenty to be seen.

Road widening of the A43 that took place soon after the removal of the SMJ bridge has destroyed trees near the road on the west side, but the old brickpit is still to be seen, filled with water, and was alleged to hide a locomotive beneath its surface. There are similar tales from half a dozen such places up and down the country, of differing degrees of credibility. In the present instance the rumours are alas, false. George Freeston unearthed a photograph of the old pit, with some of the equipment visible — narrow gauge track, cables, rollers etc, but no locomotive. The claypit has near vertical sides running down to a depth of some 60 feet, and is now used by the Towcester District Angling Association and by the police for the training of skin-divers. A police sergeant in charge of the Northampton County Constabulary skin-diving team told Fred Dix that his team practised in this flooded pit and had found therein rails in position and some tubs and even a 'rotted railway coach' used as a workman's hut in days gone by; but of a locomotive — 'definitely not'. George Freeston was a visitor also on some of these occasions, and saw a small window from the coach. It is interesting to record that in the torrid summer of 1976, when Pitsford Reservoir went

Easton Neston Quarries. The brickpit with narrow gauge track and cable rollers. This pit is now completely filled with water, and rumours of a submerged locomotive have been disproved! (Collection George Freeston)

completely dry, this pool remained full.[2] It is surrounded by boskage and on the northwest side can be seen the final gullet of the ironstone working, with an overburden of about 40 ft., on top of a layer of ironstone about 10ft. thick, still visible. A short distance at the southern end has been filled in with rubbish and with some of the mound of excavated material at the side (1983). The rest of the gullet remains much as it was left apart from heavy growth.

The remains on the east side of the road are less spectacular, geologically speaking, but more interesting from the railway point of view. The site of the earlier workings at Catchgate are mostly clothed with trees as at Catchgate Plantation, but the course of the tramway is still very well defined, even to ironstone faces, and there are traces of the working area in the adjacent sunken ground north of the Plantation. It will be noted that the broad gullet to the southeast corner of the Plantation is on a higher level than the main route, which was evidently excavated deeper in the second phase of operations. The bridge under the road, of red brick, is still in position, but the stables that stood by the bridge were demolished in 1982-84; these stables consisted of two parallel buildings sporting 'pots' like a locomotive shed, and the southern section was built slightly in front of the bridge. Between the bridge and the course of the SMJR are the calcine banks of deep red soil; the tramway up to it was carried over the line from Catchgate by a wooden bridge, but this was removed about 1981 for an access road for lorries removing calcine (for colouring tiles?) and other estate work. The tramway thence to the A43 crossing can faintly be made out along the front of the cottages, which are on sunken ground from early excavations. One curious building, whose purpose is not known, stands high on the edge of the calcine bank; it is a narrow brick building with one large arch with dog-tooth brickwork along the top, and two smaller arches in a curved wall, the whole surmounted by limestone blocks. In later years the main arch was used to house a messroom of brick with a corrugated iron roof, obscuring the original function of the building — whatever it was! The most plausible theory is that it was an experimental kiln designed by Mr. Harry, but never used — and after his death, forgotten.

The limestone slabs of the later tipping dock alongside the SMJR siding were extant until 1983, when the latter site was excavated and widened and concreted to form a silage pit, revealing a brick wall probably associated with the earlier tipping dock. Further east, the tramway route to shallow opencast pits was perfectly clear again up to 1983, when the fields were put under the plough; even so, the final gullet is still there, though being filled with the usual rubbish. There was also a pit by the Showsley

Easton Neston Quarries. The fancy brickwork of the building put up by Richard Harry, its prupose unknown — possibly an experimental limekiln. 1983.　　　　(L. V. Bootman)

road but there is doubt as to whether it was connected by rail to the Easton Neston system.

Finally, there is the standard gauge line from the pits west of the road to Towcester ironworks; this made a much bigger impression on the ground and to this day is traceable throughout its length to the similarly abandoned Towcester-Blisworth line. As already mentioned, efforts were evidently made to keep this line as level as possible, and the middle section is in cutting deeper than usual for industrial tramways of the period. Even so, the formation is not quite of main-line standard — as can very conveniently be seen by looking at the remains of the Towcaster-Olney Junction line a hundred yards or so to the east! The cutting portion is heavily choked with bushes, but lengths at ground level are either grassed over or have a sheet of water between hedges. The site of Towcester Ironworks is a hummocky waste raised above road level, now with nothing more mechanical than a windpump. The site of the locomotive shed can be seen, but not really identified, beyond the level crossing.

Footnotes

1.　　　　Proceedings of the Geological Association, 1921, p.112
2.　　　　See *Industrial Railway Record*. Vol 2, p.220.

Grid References

First system with standard gauge connection to Towcester Ironworks

708507	Tipping dock ng to sg
707508	sg level crossing with Blisworth-Towcester road
699505	Intermediate bridge
693504	Ironworks
692505	sg locomotive shed
709510	Quarry ng terminus south of road
709508	Quarry ng terminus in Plantation
708508	Level crossing

Second system with standard gauge connection to SMJR at Easton Neston

707509	Level crossing with Blisworth-Towcester road
705513	Terminus of 'Russia' Pit
706510	Brickpit
706508	Locomotive shed
708508	Bridge under road to 'Canada' Pit

Locomotives

Tramway to Towcester Ironworks (1874-1902)
Gauge; 4ft. 8½in.

FORWARD	0-6-0ST	IC	HE	119	1874	12 x 18in.	3ft. 1in.	New 2/1874	(1)
	0-4-0ST	OC	HC	427	1894	13 x 18in.	3ft. 0in.	New 12/1894	(2)

(1) to Stanton Ironworks Co Ltd, Stanton.
(2) to Woolpit Brick & Tile Co Ltd, Suffolk c 1902.

Tramway to SMJ Siding (1914-28)
Gauge; 2ft. 6in.

FERRET II	0-4-0ST	OC	WB	1853	1908	7 x 12in.	1ft. 9½in.		(a)	(1)
RYDER GIBSON	0-4-0ST	OC	WB	2103	1919	7 x 12in.	1ft. 9in.	New 7/1919		(2)

(a) ex A. C. Bealey & Sons Ltd, Radcliffe, Lancashire, via E. C. Cornforth, dealer, c 12/1914.

(1) to Blackwell & Son, Cotton End, Northampton c 1919; to Holm & Co Ltd, Kingsnorth, Kent, 1925.
(2) to Thos W. Ward Ltd, 1928; to Hendy Merthyr Colliery Co Ltd, Felin Fran.

Quarry Machines

No. 12	S. Navvy Crane	RP	390	1914	2 Cu.Yd.		New 5/1914	s/s
No. 4	SND Transporter	RP	398	1914			New 5/1914	s/s

WESTERN GROUP

Ironstone was discovered at an early date on the high ground in the neighbourhood of Church Stowe, and two small ironworks were erected alongside the LNWR main line about two miles south of Weedon station, short of the entrance to Stowe Hill tunnel. The earlier was Heyford Ironworks, first recorded in MS for 1857, though there is a possibility of its having been opened earlier; Benjamin Higgins (*Mining Journal*, 13th October 1855, p.651) refers to smelting at Heyford, though this might have been a trial. The works lay east of the railway and south of the bridge over the lane from Watling Street to Nether Heyford; the proprietor, George Pell, lived at Heyford Hills, and worked a small quarry on his land, but most of the ore for the works came from the Blisworth area. West of the railway, and north of the bridge just mentioned, lay Stowe Ironworks, first put into blast in 1866, and with direct connection to quarries near Stowe Nine Churches. Both works and quarries suffered from the stop/start policy so common in Victorian times, depending on the state of the iron trade; in the case of Stowe there were changes in ownership reflecting this financial insecurity. Both works were closed in the slump of the early 1890s and were subsequently dismantled.

Two miles south of the old Northampton and now rapidly being engulfed by the new Northampton, ironstone was worked in the early 1850s, contemporaneously with the Blisworth district; but the area has not been generally credited with this anywhere, in contrast to Duston, where the management seem to have attracted press attention continually in the early days. Hunsbury Hill was a little later, but received attention by reason of the ironworks in the past, and in recent years as a railway preservation centre.

HEYFORD QUARRY

Owners: Pell & Co

This is quoted in MS as 'Heyford.Pell & Co' and as operating 1863-68; it is not more particularly identified, but could be at Heyford Hills, where Pell is known to have extracted ironstone. At the back of Pell's old home at Heyford Hills there is distinct evidence of former quarrying activity in the sunken fields below the hedge, but no evidence of a tramway; in any case, it would have needed a funicular to reach the LNWR directly. Such a line might have existed (and it must be remembered that rail haulage for minerals was almost always preferable to using the indifferent roads of the period) but it has left no visible traces—just the quarry site. There is still, however, alongside the siding to the main line, a wall that could have retained a tipping arrangement.

Grid References

656574   Quarry site

STOWE NINE CHURCHES QUARRIES

Owners: Northamptonshire Ironstone Co: Stowe Iron Ore Co from 1863: Castle Dykes Iron Ore Co Ltd from 1867: Nine Churches Iron Ore Co from 1875.

The ironstone quarries listed as 'Stowe Nine Churches' or just simply 'Stowe' in the standard reference works were small and insignificant, but the history of the tramways that served them was extremely complex. That there was a tramway at all was first brought to our notice by the brief reference in NSI, pp.193/4 — 'Ore was exploited between 1916 and 1920 in Lodge Plantation ... and the material was conveyed by tramway to the now abandoned Stowe Furnaces'. Starting with this vital clue (the route was correct though the dates were erroneous) we were able, with the generous help of local people, to compile the account given in *IRTM*, with the proviso that it might have to be revised should further material be brought to light. Such has been the case concerning the change of gauge of the tramway. There is no reasonable doubt that the original line was a narrow gauge one running to the canal, superseded by a standard gauge connection to the LNWR; but local testimony of a vertical-boilered locomotive on the narrow gauge was at variance with statements in *Tales of Stowe* and other sources that strongly suggested a standard gauge line in the 1870s. The identification of the VB locomotive as a standard gauge machine resolved that matter, while the fact that the line was opened considerably earlier than 1863 makes the conversion to standard gauge by 1870 more readily acceptable. So things fall into place rather more tidily now; but we would not claim finality yet!

With some reluctance we have discarded the title 'Lodge Plantation Quarries' adopted in *IRTM* in favour of that appearing in official records, and because the description 'Plantation' only applied after quarrying had ceased.

Having explained why this account differs from the earlier one, it is time to get down to details of this, which ranks among the earliest (and, at the time, longest) of the ironstone quarry lines.

It has already been said that in the formative years of the East Midlands ironstone industry it is unwise to place complete reliance upon the at other times generally acceptable data in MS. Hunt could only record what he was told, and until the industry was established he had few sources of information to tap. For the early 1850s, therefore, we must look elsewhere for our data and then see how it fits in with what Hunt has to say a few years later. *Mining Journal* for 2nd July 1853 and the following two weeks carried a rather curious advertisement by an also curiously named body, in the following terms:

'To Ironmasters, Iron Ore Dealers and Others

Notice is hereby given that the GOVERNORS of the CORPORATION of the SONS OF THE CLERGY are prepared to receive TENDERS for the IRON ORE on the estate at STOWE NINE CHURCHES in the county of Northampton. The ore is very abundant, of fine quality, and lies within a few feet of the surface. The estate comprises about 1,700 acres and is most conveniently situated for carriage, a portion skirting the London & North-Western Railway, about one mile south of the Weedon station. Easy access to the Grand Junction Canal may also be obtained by agreement with other parties.

Tenders must be sent in for the consideration of the Governors on or before Friday 22nd July next, and may be made for any portion not less than 20 acres of the ore. The Governors do not undertake to accept the highest offer. Plans of the estate, and any further particulars may be obtained by application to Chas John Baker, Registrar, 2 Bloomsbury Place, London.

June 28, 1853.'

The reference to access by rail and canal explains a map in Northamptonshire Record Office, dated 1853, of the Corporation's estates in Stowe Nine Churches and Lower Heyford, showing the locations of 17 trial holes dug in the search for iron ore, the greatest concentration being in the area west of the road near Stowe Lodge; and from a point here four alternative routes by which the ironstone might be transferred from the site — to the canal or to the LNWR either east or west of Stowe tunnel. The note at the foot of the map adds that these 'appear to be the most eligible for tramways to the railway and canal, and can be constructed to other parts of the estate'. There appears to have been an earlier tramway on the Corporation's land for conveying limestone to a wharf by Watling Street on the west side and possibly to Stowe Wharf, where there were kilns. The ironstone line probably utilized and extended the same track. The 1853 map shows tramway originating not at the Lodge Plantation site (at that time open ground) but to the north of the lane to Stowe village, with the tramway crossing the lane on the level. The line as built, however, kept to the south of the lane.

The question of who took up the Corporation's offer, and opened up the quarries in the 1850s is nowhere (so far as we know) named specifically, but was almost certainly the Northamptonshire Ironstone Co., who on 30th April 1853 invited applications for shares (*Mining Journal*, 30th April 1853). The office is quoted as the Moot Hall, Daventry, and applications were to be in by 2nd May 1853. MS for 1855 quotes Northampton, Blisworth and Weedon, the entry being repeated for 1856/7, and Weedon (as the nearest railway station) may reasonably be equated to Stowe Nine Churches. In 1857 the list of blast furnaces quoted Heyford (Weedon) — Pell & Co, and in 1858 the same information with a note 'supplied from Gayton', possibly implying that before then the furnaces had been supplied from elsewhere, presumably 'Weedon'. The areas Northampton, Blisworth and Weedon are given in 1855/6 with a collective labour force, suggesting common ownership; if this is so, then it seems likely that the owners were Northamptonshire Ironstone Co[1], which was associated with Pell (*Mining Journal* of 13th October 1855 refers to smelting at Heyford and to the Northamptonshire Iron Co, owned by Pell). Bearing in mind the comments made above, quarrying may have commenced in 1853 or 1854, but certainly was in being in 1855; *Geological Survey Memoirs* 1917-27 refers to 'early workings at Church Stowe 1855-1865'. The workforce at Weedon in 1857 is given by Robert Hunt as one only, and there are no further references to this location, so it seems that quarrying ceased from 1857 to 1863 — doubtless partly due to the erratic situation at Heyford ironworks (see below).

Quarrying recommenced at Stowe Nine Churches in 1863 under the ownership of Stowe Iron Ore Co. The tramway ran to a wharf alongside the Grand Junction Canal at Nether Heyford, after the fashion of the Blisworth lines already described, passing under the LNWR by means of a brick arch; thence the line ran to the canal, whereby the ore was presumably conveyed the short distance to Heyford ironworks, unless the line was extended along the canal bank. There is a difference in altitude between the canal and the Stowe Hills of some 240ft., resulting in a stiff bank from the bridge under Watling Street though a coppice to the rear of Stowe School, where the tramway crossed the footpath to Upper Stowe; this section was worked as a double-acting incline by cable, the descending full wagons drawing up the empties. The section from the incline summit to the quarries was probably worked by horses, though locomotive power cannot definitely be excluded, and the gauge of the rails was about 1ft. 9in. or possibly 2ft.

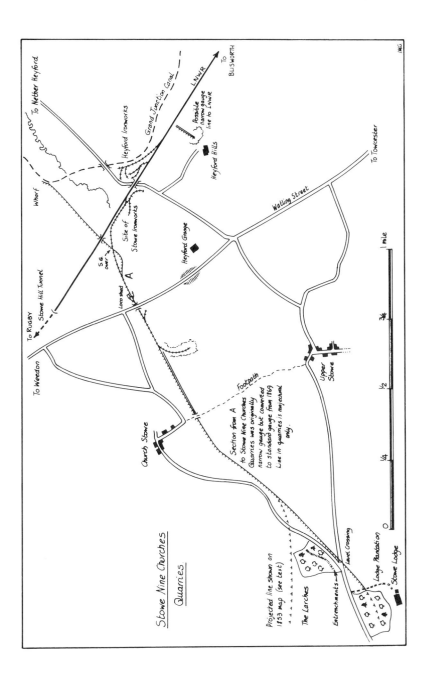

Stowe Nine Churches Quarries. The quarries were served originally by a narrow gauge tramway to the canal, passing beneath the LNWR by the bridge (left); this was replaced by a standard gauge line connecting with the LNWR at a higher level (right). 1955.

(G. H. Starmer)

Thus far the story is fairly straightforward; the details given have been vouched for independently by four local men and are consistent with probabilities — the narrow gauge, the route to the canal, etc — but soon after Castle Dykes Iron Ore Co Ltd took over operations in 1867 matters became more complex. They replaced the narrow gauge line by one of standard gauge connecting with the LNWR (an alternative, it will be remembered, suggested by the lessors of the ground). This was done probably in 1869 or 1870; the records of Chaplin & Co Ltd, the Glasgow locomotive builders, state that their No. 1056 was supplied new in 1869 to D. Murray, Blisworth, and was owned by the Castle Dykes Iron Ore Co by 1870. There does not appear to have been a resident of this name in Blisworth at this time, so it is most likely that Murray was a contractor responsible for laying the new standard gauge line and that he sold the locomotive to the iron ore company on completion of the work.

Mining Journal of 30th December 1871 carried an announcement of the proposed formation of the Castle Dykes Iron Co Ltd to take over as one concern the quarries of the Castle Dykes Iron Ore Co Ltd and Stowe Furnaces though an agreement dated 18th October 1871 with William McClure, the proprietor of the latter; the description of the properties stated that 'the mines were connected by a tramway about one and a half miles in length with the main line of the LNWR, so that railway wagons can be run up to the pits and the ore loaded directly into them... a commodious siding has been laid adjoining the main line. A large sum of money has been expended in opening and developing the mines and making the tramway... two locomotives have been purchased'. Henry E. Taylor of the consulting firm of John Taylor & Sons inspected the works and suggested that to improve efficiency 'the incline plane be done away with and the gradient reduced to, say, 1 in 40 to allow a locomotive to pass up it with railway trucks. One tank engine from 14 to 16 tons could do all the work with the assistance of horses to tram from short sidings in the quarry'. The first of these statements suggests that standard railway wagons ran directly to the pits, while the second clearly refers to the cable-worked incline; so the general modus operandi was fundamentally the same as the narrow gauge. The identity of the second locomotive is unknown, but probably it worked the lower section connecting with the LNWR. The Chaplin locomotive was remembered by very old inhabitants as working the upper section from incline summit to the quarries; they did not recall the name of the maker but said that the locomotive had four coupled wheels and a vertical boiler between the frames and was therefore referred to as 'The Coffeepot' — it apparently had no official name. This description conforms to that of a Chaplin so closely as to leave no room for doubt. The new tramway did not go underneath the LNWR, but curved round in a southerly direction to Stowe Furnaces and, further, was embanked towards its eastern terminus, thus to bring the wagons to a suitable height for discharging directly into limekilns, as limestone was also worked. It is this embankment that was primarily responsible for obliterating traces of the former narrow gauge line at ground level.

The history of the quarries is closely bound up with the fortunes of the two ironworks; before 1866 Heyford Ironworks only were operating, hence the route of the narrow gauge tramway to the canal instead of the LNWR; in 1866 Stowe Ironworks on the side of the LNWR nearer to Stowe were put in blast but worked for a few months only and were then closed until 1873 following 'reconstruction' by William McClure in the previous year. Since the Stowe quarries worked continuously from 1863 to 1872, it is fair to assume that the output went as usual to Heyford Ironworks and that drastic changes in the equipment are unlikely to have taken place; such improvements would naturally be left to the new CDIO Co Ltd to carry out. In the event, the 1871 scheme fell through (it was struck off the Register of Companies on 30th September 1884), Stowe Ironworks continuing to be owned by McClure and the quarries by CDIO Co Ltd, but the latter are stated in a letter to Stowe Parish Council as having closed in September 1892 and are quoted in MS for 1873/4 as 'standing' i.e. idle. Heyford Ironworks offered comparatively steady employment but suffered temporary closures in each of the years 1859/63/66/67; this seems to have been due to the shaky financial position of the owners (quoted variously as Pell & Co and George Pell), a position unsecured by the formation of a limited company (The Heyford Co Ltd) in 1865, and in the end only retrieved by the intervention of C. H. Plevins, the proprietor of Islip Ironworks, who took over in 1870[2] and finally put matters on a solid basis by forming the Heyford Iron Co Ltd in March 1874. Pell and his associates also had quarries at Heyford Hills (Pell's own estate) from 1863-68, at Gayton from 1855 onwards, and at Duston from 1873-76, so that the Heyford furnaces were by no means dependent on the Stowe quarries for supplies. In 1873 Stowe Ironworks were in use, but where their ore came from we do not know; possibly from the Gayton/Blisworth area where there were already several operators.

In 1875 two significant events occurred; first, William McClure purchased a new standard gauge locomotive from Manning Wardle; and secondly, the Nine Churches Iron Ore Co came into being, with quarries at 'Nine Churches' (Stowe Nine Churches is the full name of the village) which presumably were the same ones. The new company acquired a standard gauge six-coupled Manning Wardle secondhand, in 1875 presumably, replacing the locomotive already on the lower section of line.

Regarding the location of Stowe ironstone quarries, there is nothing to suggest that they were elsewhere than at 'Lodge Plantation'. Stowe Furnaces were in blast in 1875/6, after which they were closed until 1890, and an output of iron ore is recorded from 'Nine Churches' quarries for those two years and none later. In a very interesting little book of local history written by the schoolmaster's son, Leonard Ladkin — called 'Tales of Stowe' and published in Everdon in 1922 — it is stated that the section of line 'from Stowe to Stowe Lodge' was closed in 1878, which suggests that the ironstone came from Stowe Lodge. He also recalls one runaway on the incline; 'Three loaded wagons once tore down the steep slope of two miles and came to a stand close to the LNWR down main line. A passenger train was passing and the footboards were torn away from the train's entire length'.

There is very little doubt that quarrying for ironstone ceased in the period 1876-78 and thenceforward the line extended only as far as the limestone quarry in the coppice just west of Watling Street. Nothing further is heard of the Nine Churches Iron Ore Co after 1877, hence they presumably went out of business, and their locomotive was offered for sale in August 1877 (*Iron* 25th August 1877 — thanks to Messrs M & D Stoyel for this item). It seems likely that they had taken over the Chaplin locomotive from their predecessors, for this is recorded by the makers as being with Henry Mobbs, Vulcan Ironworks, Northampton in 1878, presumably from an enquiry for

Stowe Nine Churches Quarries. In its later days, as Nether Heyford brickworks owned by the Blisworth & Stowe Brick and Tile Co Ltd, traffic was worked by this 1872 Aveling & Porter loco. from the Oxford and Aylesbury Tramroad (later Brill tramway). Kilns may be seen to the left. 27th March 1951.
(C. P. Knight)

spares. Mobbs may have used it themselves but more likely simply purchased it for resale. Apparently it did not move very far but was acquired by the Blisworth & Stowe Brick & Tile Co Ltd to operate their Gayton brickworks (see under Gayton Quarries). To be precise, we had better say that a Chaplin locomotive was noted here in derelict condition for some years in the late 1920s or early 1930s by Mr. C. R. H. Simpson, who lived locally. He did not note the maker's number, but the comparative rarity of Chaplins makes it unlikely to be any locomotive other than the Castle Dykes machine. The remaining portions of the tramway were kept in operation however, and were worked by the locomotive attached to Stowe Furnaces. The latter commenced — under new management — steel production in 1890 but were closed in 1892, though the tramway continued in use for the conveyance of limestone to the kilns until 1900. *Tales of Stowe* records that in 1920 the track was lifted from the quarry to the point where the embankment curved towards the works, the site of which was acquired by Geo. King & Son (later the Blisworth & Stowe Brick and Tile Co Ltd), who commenced the manufacture of bricks from the underlying clay; the premises again changed hands on 22nd March 1923, when they were purchased as a going concern by Henry Martin Ltd of Northampton. A 2ft. 11in. gauge tramway was built the short distance between the brickworks and the claypits but the chief interest resided in the standard gauge motive power, which consisted of the two early Aveling & Porter geared locomotives once used on the Oxford & Aylesbury tramroad (later the Metropolitan Railway's Brill Branch). Later, one of these was rebuilt to incorporate the better parts of its partner, and this ancient machine carried out its duties, staggering up the bank to the LMSR with one or two laden wagons at a time, until the brickworks were closed in 1940, when the yard was requisitioned by the War Department for ammunition storage; the engine was later ejected from its shed and its rusting carcase became a familiar if unusual sight to travellers on the LMSR main line. From this unhappy plight it was rescued through the perseverance of the Industrial Locomotive Society, who were instrumental in arranging for it to be preserved by London Transport, whose predecessors had owned the O&AT (better known as the Brill Tramway).

To end this tale (we have already departed from ironstone associations, but feel it to be justified by the interest attached) mention should be made of the fact that Stowe lime quarries were reopened in comparatively recent times by a local farming family named Faulkner, who built kilns on the spot and also quarried stone for building purposes; their steam crane was still to be seen in the 1950s, derelict in the woods surrounding the old pits. In this case rail transport was not used. Stone from here was used in restoration work on Castle Ashby church and house in 1982; it is said that two pieces weighed 11½ tons!

The course of the standard gauge tramway is still clear for most of the route, starting at the main line end by the tree-lined embankment that descends to ground level as it approaches the bridge under Watling Street. There has been redevelopment, in the postwar period, of the former ironworks site as a small industrial estate that has swept away the overgrown bases of the old brickworks kilns, but so far this has not encroached on the tramway. The narrow gauge remains however disappeared almost completely in recent years; the point of divergence from the standard gauge route of the preceding narrow gauge line, leading to a bridge under the BR line, was clearly traceable, but in September 1973 the bridge was filled in and the embankment towards it mostly removed; nevertheless, a short stub remains, close to the standard gauge embankment and is most clearly viewed from passing trains. North of the BR line the route to the canal was less obvious as it was at ground level, and the faint traces that could be seen alongside the hedge have now gone. The canal wharf area is built up by earth and is now a patch of overgrown ground. The narrow gauge is however faintly visible in the field north of Watling Street; the standard gauge embankment is fully extant and a hundred yards or so to the west can be seen the curved line of the narrow gauge at field level, cutting across the ancient agricultural 'ridge and furrow'.

Stowe Nine Churches Quarries. Site of bridge under the Stowe tramway, used for farming access. 12th April 1975. (Eric Tonks)

Stowe Nine Churches Quarries. Bridge under the A5, west portal, 27th April 1988. Behind the branch over the middle of the parapet is a stone slab, with a coat of arms, presumably that of the Corporation of the Sons of the Clergy, the landowners. This slab is now much defaced. (A. Cocklin)

Back at the Watling Street bridge; nearby was a wooden building that is believed to have been the old Castle Dykes and Nine Churches locomotive shed, as early OS maps show rail tracks running into it, and there are traces of what seems to be a bricked recess in the ground near the door, that was possibly the site of the water supply. It didn't *look* much like a locomotive shed, but the slight positive evidence and lack of any alternative location (on maps, for example) point in the same direction. Unfortunately it was not best constructed to last and in the 1970s was becoming increasingly

Stowe Nine Churches Quarries. The locomotive shed used presumably by the Chaplin locomotive on the standard gauge line, here viewed from the Watling Street bridge. The line continued between the avenue of trees. 1955. (G. H. Starmer)

dilapidated; by 1973 it had lost its roof and was demolished the following summer, replaced by a modern farm building more or less on the same site. Happily, the nearby bridge is still in position, though a quick glance from the railway side would suggest that it has been replaced by a modern structure; in fact, the bridge has been widened (in 1969, it is thought) and the east side is of reinforced concrete with a parapet of green painted railings. The west side is in its original condition with the unexpected embellishment in stone of a coat of arms (that of the Sons of the Clergy, it may be presumed) that is almost hidden by foliage in summer. The bridge seems to be used mainly as an open-ended shed for farm implements.

The site of the incline is well defined but marshy at the bottom and overgrown in the middle where it passes through a belt of trees, but easier to trace at the top where it forms a 'nick' in the hillside. The latter levels out towards the footpath between the two Stowes and, beyond, the path the ground is level, and there are no further traces until the road junction is reached. There is a very clear definition of the route as a depression across the field south of the level crossing site towards the drive to Stowe Lodge and even more deeply marked in Lodge Plantation, where also working faces can be seen (with difficulty in the undergrowth!). Lodge Plantation, it may be assumed, was planted to cover up the scars left by the early workings. Where the tramway route crossed the drive to Stowe Lodge there is no 'dip' now—presumably it was levelled—and a lime tree (one of an avenue along the drive) is growing in the course of the line; however, as nearly a hundred years has elapsed since working ceased, there would be plenty of time for a tree of this stature to grow!

'The Larches' on the other side of the road—now disfigured by a dump of abandoned cars—is shown on maps as a site of archaeological interest, and so is Castle Dykes earthworks. The name Castle Dykes Iron Ore Co suggests that the company considered quarrying here, and the ground certainly appears to be iron-bearing; but there is no evidence of it ever being done—none in living memory anyway, and there is no trace of any tramway, which in the troubled terrain would be pretty sure to leave some reminders.

West of Watling Street there are parts of the old lime kilns surviving and between here and the later quarry east south east of Stowe church a piece of flat-bottomed rail protruding from what is now a trackway, was found by an industrial archaeology group (under Mr. G. H. Starmer's tutelage) in 1974. The later quarry seems to have cut through the old line of tramway, since one can see the section of the cutting emerging into the later quarry, with the bottom of the cutting about 8ft. above the bottom of the more recent quarry. The width and extent of the workings seems to be on a remarkably large scale for limestone.

Footnotes

1. The book of *Rules and Regulations* is in the Northamptonshire Record Office, and is lettered 'Northamptonshire Iron Company', indicating a change of title; the office was still at Daventry, and the blank pages are filled with records from Daventry Petty Sessions, 1888-1895!

2. *Mining Journal*, 28th May 1870, p.457.

Grid References

Narrow Gauge tramway

653583	Canal Wharf
650580	Bridge under LNWR
647578	Bridge under Watling Street
646575	Top of incline

Standard gauge tramway

652579	Connection with LMSR
650579	Point where sg route deviates from former ng route
649579	Accommodation bridge in embankment
647578	Locomotive shed
644575	Limestone Quarry
652578	Stowe Ironworks
630574	Level crossing of drive to Stowe Lodge
629563	Lodge Plantation quarries

Summary of tramway history

c 1854-1857	Northamptonshire Ironstone Co)	Narrow gauge tramway to canal,
1863-1866	Stowe Iron Ore Co)	probably horse worked
1867-1868	Castle Dykes Iron Ore Co Ltd)	
1869-1872	Castle Dykes Iron Ore Co Ltd	Standard gauge tramway to LNWR. Locomotive haulage.
1873-1874		Tramway idle.
1875-1876	Nine Churches Iron Ore Co	Standard gauge tramway to Stowe Ironworks. Locomotive haulage.
1878		Upper section from limepits to Lodge Plantation removed.
1876(?)-1900		Lower section worked for limestone by locomotive from Stowe Ironworks.
1920		Section from brickworks to limepits removed.
1900(?)-1940		Remainder worked by locomotive from brickworks.

Locomotives

Gauge; 4ft. 8½in.

Castle Dykes Iron Ore Co
COFFEEPOT   0-4-0TG VB Chaplin 1056 1869   (a) (1)

(a) ex D. Murray, Blisworth, 1870.

(1) to Henry Mobbs, Vulcan Ironworks, Northampton by 1878.

Nine Churches Iron Ore Co
CARLISLE   0-6-0ST IC MW   428   1873 12 x 17in.   3ft.0in.   (a) (1)

(a) ex John Bayliss, contractor, Settle and Carlisle line, 1875.

(1) to MW (?), 8/1877; later to Monk & Edwards, contractors.

Wm. McClure
IRON DUKE   0-4-0ST OC MW   537   1875 12 x 18in.   3ft. 0in.   New 3/1875 (1)

(1) to Lever Bros Ltd, Cheshire, via King & Smith, c 1900.

Henry Martin Ltd
.   0-4-0TG G AP   807   1872 7¾ x 10in.   3ft. 0in.   (a) (1)
.   0-4-0TG G AP   846   1872 7¾ x 10in.   3ft. x 0in.   (a) Scr

(a) ex Oxford & Aylesbury Tramroad, 1894.

(1) Purchased for preservation by the Industrial Locomotive Society; to LTE Neasden 3/1951 for restoration, later to South Kensington Museum.

Stowe Nine Churches Quarries.
Former tramway route in Lodge Plantation, looking south-southeast, 12th April 1975.   (Eric Tonks)

DUSTON QUARRIES

Owners: Duston Iron Ore Co: George Pell from 1859: G. E. Bevan & Co Ltd from 1863 and Northampton Iron Ore Co from 1872: Henry Higgins from 1880: Duston Iron Ore Co Ltd from 28th February 1885.

By and large, iron ore companies did not seek publicity, but were content to get on with the job in hand; occasionally obituaries would appear in the local press when a quarry closed down, this being particularly the case in the 1960s, otherwise most concerns were born, lived and died without a public mention on paper. With one exception: the Duston Iron Ore Co positively courted publicity, and there are mentions of it in various sources that have survived in archives; they give us valuable information about the history of the company and an insight into the iron ore industry at the time.

Ironstone was discovered at Duston at a very early date — at least by 1851 and possibly by 1849, when in the course of work on the turnpike road near Duston traces of a Roman burial ground and quantities of pottery were found. The seam of stone was reputedly the thickest in the Midlands — said in old records to have been about 30ft., though this is thought to be an exaggeration — so it is little wonder that the area was exploited as soon as the possibility of supplying the ironmasters of Staffordshire and Derbyshire showed promise.

Duston Iron Ore Co was formed by a partnership of two London chemists, Thomas Lucas and John Carter Lucas, and was so registered on 11th September 1854, with H. S. Lucas as managing director; but the company title was in use before this, when the partners were examining the site, taking samples for analysis, and planning means of moving the ore to prospective customers. The partners negotiated a lease with Henry John Viscount Palmerston and Emily Mary Viscountess Palmerston, his wife, for a term of thirty years from 25th March 1854. It was proposed to connect the quarries by tramway to the LNWR Northampton-Blisworth line, with a short branch to the Grand Junction Canal en route. There are references to the latter in the diary of Mr. J. Cherry, one-time canal overseer; this diary, covering the years 1854-57, is in the possession of George Freeston, and specimen extracts follow:-

'10 July 1854.

Per train to Northampton to meet the Rev. Cox and the Manager of the Duston Iron Ore Co. taking a survey of the proposed line of rail to cross the canal per bridge per application of Mr. Lucas, also obtained information regarding a landing for loading Iron stone into boats, and the transit of ditto by rail.

Feb. 21 1855

Walked to Northampton & Duston making enquiry respecting the owners & occupiers of land in connection with the canal at Duston Bridge and also with the line of rail belonging to the Duston Iron Ore Co. per order of Mr Rogers etc.

Feb. 24 1855

... inspected Bridge No. 13 the way in which the Duston Iron Ore Co. crossed the bridge...

May 10 1855

... thence to Duston to see Mr. Nichols with regard concerning the obstruction in loading boats with iron ore.'

A formal Agreement dated 30th November 1854 between the Duston Iron Ore Co and the canal company provided for a 200 yard siding, with a section along the canal side 10ft. wide — 4ft. on the bank and 6ft. supported on piles over the water. Use of these facilities was for one year from 25th December 1854, and renewable annually.

This Agreement is preserved in the Northamptonshire Record Office, along with another rather curious document in the form of a License, dated 7th February 1855, by a committee appointed by H. M. Privy Council, authorizing the company to lease land for quarrying at Duston. The area concerned was about 1300 acres. We have not seen a like document relating to other quarries, so possibly it was a short-lived requirement. The plan attached is useful in indicating the tramway layout.

The implication that the Duston Iron Ore Co's tramway was laid towards the end of 1854 is confirmed by a report to the shareholders' meeting held on 1st November 1854 and printed in *Mining Journal* of the 4th: 'The railway to connect the property with the canal and the London and North-Western line he (Mr. Thomas Lucas, Managing Director) expected to be completed by the middle of this month'. The canal wharf had been obtained with a frontage of 200 yards. The report continues: 'The gradients of the line were so favourable that the wagons would run to the River Nene without expense for motive power, and only one or two horses would be required to arrange trucks on the railway'. Further information was given in the reports of the official 'Opening Ceremony' that took place on 1st January 1855. The holding of an opening ceremony is itself remarkable; perhaps there have been others but the only ones we know were at Desborough (1905) and Harlaxton (1943). The directors and principal shareholders assembled at the George Hotel and proceeded to Duston at noon, where the ceremony was opened by prayers offered by the Rev. R. H. Cox, vicar of Duston; two wagons were present, one loaded with six tons of ore, the other to accommodate the party, who then 'proceeded down the line'. Having arrived at 'The Siding'. the chairman, Thomas Bisgood, declared the works open; the navvies were informed that refreshment awaited them at the works, while the directors and party took themselves back to the 'George' for a 'sumptuous dinner', followed by several evidently lengthy speeches (the report in the *Northampton Mercury* of 6th January 1855 covers more than two full columns). However, let us be grateful for these speeches, for in them is a lot of fresh information, summarized in the next two paragraphs.

The ground was leased from Lord and Lady Palmerston and in extent was nearly 100 acres, of which 30 were in Glebe; thus explaining the interest of the Rev. Cox in the enterprise, both here and earlier with the canal overseer. The Weedon road intersected the property, which was bounded on the north by the two roads to Duston village, but at this date most of the developments were south of the Weedon road, where excavations had commenced and a 'railroad' constructed in three months, 'particularly substantial and well made' and 1468 yards in length. The railway was on an incline as far as the canal bridge, such that loaded wagons would descend by their own momentum to that point, or nearly so. Sidings capable of holding 40-50 empty wagons were laid, as was a similar set for laden wagons.

Discovery of the ore was attributed to Thomas Lucas, who also found clay on the site, and buildings were in course of erection for the manufacture of bricks by Clayton's Patent Process. Mr. Lucas, while modestly refraining from claiming the discovery, did refer to the finding of coins marked with the head of the Emperor Claudius, on the site (This was in 1854, according to *Victoria County History*, Vol I, 1902, p.197). Mr. Lucas went on to announce that the brickworks were to be commissioned on 1st March and that the foundations of two furnaces were to be erected in a field north of Weedon Road about the same time. Limestone was also available and would be worked if a reduction in the royalty payable could be achieved. It will be noted that Thomas Lucas was now managing director in place of H. S.

Lucas, and possibly there were other changes in management.

Another speaker with something to say was Mr. Bond, present in his capacity of mineral agent for Lord Palmerston, but speaking more from his associations with the firm of Bond & Matthews, Corbyns Hall Ironworks, near Dudley. He was well aware of the prejudice held by some Staffordshire ironmasters concerning Northamptonshire ore, and knew from practical experience of the difficulties inherent in changing to this source. The Duston Iron Ore Co's prospectus guaranteed to supply ore of 40% iron content, and he recommended that, to be certain of meeting this, the ore should be calcined.

Another report, from *Mining Journal* of 6th January 1855, adds some further details. Referring to the trip over the line, the report states that 'to this train several ropes were attached, and, preceded by the sawyers, carpenters, bricklayers, blacksmiths and navigators to the number of about 90, each carrying an emblem of his trade, which had a very novel but characteristic appearance, drew the party from the works to the end of the line, amidst the cheers of a numerous assemblage'. Because of the gentle incline it may be presumed that the workmen did not have to pull very hard, and were able to give some attention to holding aloft the 'emblems of their trade'! The Chairman gave £10 to be divided amongst the men. It was said that the ore was only about 3ft. below the surface and ran from to 20 to 30ft. deep.

Unfortunately, the bright promises conjured up at this meeting and in the glowing prospectus that had attracted considerable previous investment, were very soon extinguished in a welter of acrimony. Within six months it was apparent that things were seriously wrong and the board appointed a 'committee of Investigation', whose report was read before an Extraordinary General Meeting on 7th September 1855 and published in the *Northampton Mercury* the following day. The managing director, Thomas Lucas, was held primarily responsible and, having been debarred from attending the EGM, he adopted the only course open to him by stating his views in letters to the press (*Northampton Mercury*, 15th and 29th September 1855).

The poor sales of ore were probably due more to difficulties in processing at the ironworks than to inferiority of the ore itself, but the company had spent so much on activities other than simple quarrying that they were unable to continue until the technical difficulties at the furnaces had been overcome. In December 1855 the Chairman reported the very unfavourable position to the shareholders. He also reported (*Mining Journal*, 1855, p.795) that 200 wagons had been hired from the Midland Wagon Co.

It is doubtful if there was any more quarrying under the auspices of the

Duston Iron Ore Co, which was wound up in April 1859. It is perhaps significant that no archaeological finds were recorded in the years 1855-59, but plenty in 1860-70. In 1859 George Pell is quoted in MS as producing ironstone at Duston, and is stated to have acquired the leases and tramway in that year, according to the Minutes of Evidence for the Bedford, Northampton & Weedon Railway (see below). Pell's activities were taken over by the Northampton Iron Ore Co (sometimes rendered Northamptonshire Iron Co) in 1872 and ceased four years later. Pell applied to the Trustees of the Warwick & Northampton Turnpike to construct a tunnel under the main road in April 1860. Meanwhile, G. E. Bevan & Co were operating at Duston, their first recorded output being in 1863, according to MS. However, a note by William Brown in *Mining Journal* for 1861 (p.383) states that G. E. Bevan & Co are 'sending large supplies from four or five different estates in the neighbourhood' (Northamptonshire), which suggests that Duston was in production then and that Bevans took over the quarries possibly as a going concern. They continued in production until 1880. There is no doubt that from 1863 to 1872 at least, Pell and Bevan used the same tramway, which presumably had sidings to each set of workings. This confusion in ownership and operation of the quarries is reflected in the Minutes of Evidence in respect of three competing railway companies, whose Bills were considered in the 1865 session of Parliament. These were the Bedford, Northampton & Weedon, the Bedford, Northampton & Leamington, and the East & West Junction Extension, all of whose railways would have crossed, within a few yards, the Duston embankment. The three Books of Reference differ in their description of owner, lessee and occupier of this feature. George Pell gave evidence before the committee of the House of Commons, in favour of the E&WJER, and a gentleman of the same name was a solicitor of this Bill and others; so possibly this Book of Reference is the most reliable. The embankment is referred to as a 'tramway and footway' and the owner Lady Palmerston and the Board of Waywardens of the Hardingstone District; the lessee as Duston Iron Ore Co; and occupier, George Pell. G. E. Bavan is not mentioned, but the Book of Reference of the BN&LR gives the occupiers as George Pell and George Edward Bevan. Possibly the latter was in a minor capacity. G. H. Bond, described as a 'Mining Engineer' to Lord and Lady Palmerston, gave evidence for the BN&WR, in which he stated that Mr. Pell was the sole lessee of the minerals. Output was about 1500 tons per week and commenced in 1859. Presumably he meant that the present occupier started in 1859; he could hardly have forgotten his speech of 1st January 1855 at the formal opening of the Duston Iron Ore Co

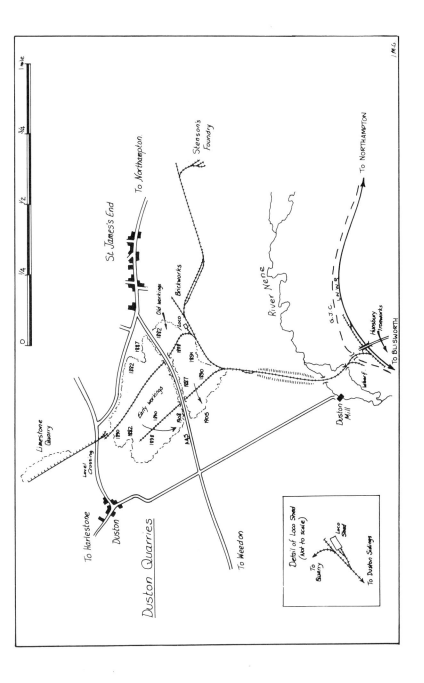

enterprise — but perhaps he preferred to draw a veil over the irregularities concerning that! The plan of the BN&WR route shows the tramway as a single track from the Nene to the engine shed junction. We are indebted to Geoffrey W. Webb for the above extracts from British Transport Historical Records; and to Geoffrey Starmer for newspaper reports.

As will be seen from the map, the standard gauge tramway was of considerable length and complexity, and appears to have been used to some extent as a common carrier, for in addition to at least two groups of ironstone quarries there was a branch to the foundry of Joseph Stenson & Co in St. James's End, traffic for which was dealt with by arrangement. F. Whellan (*History of Northamptonshire*, 1874, p.305) records that this branch was opened in 1853. The two-road locomotive shed was at the junction of Stenson's Branch. There was also a siding serving a brickworks and there is a reference to traffic from 'R. Attenborough's Works and Wharf' — but Attenborough had connections with Joseph Stenson & Co (see under Brixworth Ironstone Co) so possibly this was the same siding. By the time of the survey for the 1883 map, the siding to the canal wharf had gone.

Before describing the tramway, we might mention another member of the cloth who had some influence. The Rev. Peake Banton was Vicar of Duston from 1863 to his death in 1891, and while his predecessor offered prayers for the venture the autocratic Peake Banton continually haggled about the wayleaves over the glebeland, and tried to stop the ironstone quarrying, as Mr. Langton of Duston told Geoffrey Starmer.

The tramway left the LNWR Blisworth line by Duston Sidings Signal Box, crossed the canal by a rather humpbacked bridge, then the river by a 'viaduct' and across the marshy Nene Valley on an embankment, of considerable solidarity for a mineral line, which was pierced at intervals to allow passage for flood water. There was a passing loop on the embankment, which was constructed mainly of rubble from the quarries. The section between river and canal was carried on a series of wooden trestles. Ironstone occurred round the 250-ft. contour, and was quarried from a wide area — south of the Weedon road (A45) and north almost as far as Duston Road, both east and west (mostly the latter) served by branches from the main tramway. The 1883 OS 6in. map shows this tramway and also a lengthy extension north north west, crossing Duston Road on the level near the junction with Bant's Lane and running for a quarter mile beyond to a quarry north east of Duston village. This was a limestone quarry at the 300-ft. contour, and the extension tramway (on a higher level than the ironstone line) was of narrow gauge with a tipping dock at its southern end

Duston Quarries. The 'high lines' c 1930. The Nene was liable to periodic flooding, and the Duston tramway was carried over the low-lying area on a series of trestles. After closure, the trackbed made a useful footpath, and as such lasted until the disturbance of the site by gravel workings in the late 1960s.

(Collection G. H. Starmer)

adjacent to the standard gauge ironstone line so that tubs could be side-tipped into standard gauge wagons. We presume that Pell and his associates worked certain faces and Bevan others, but in the absence of information from leases we cannot be sure on this point.Bevan's quarries were taken over by Henry Higgins in 1880 — by this time Pell was no longer in the picture — but Higgins died in the following year, and an inventory made in September 1883 states that the railway comprised nearly two miles of track, 286 wagons (mostly of 6 and 8 ton types), two locomotives and the usual quarrying equipment, but financially the system was in poor shape and the executors decided to rid themselves of it; when no immediate purchaser could be found, legal complications caused further delay and loss, and a sale of surplus equipment was held in December 1884 when, amongst other things, the Midland Railway purchased 150 8-ton wagons at £29 each. A new company took over the remainder as a going concern, and with continuation of other traffic, on 28th February 1885 — paying 7/- per yard for the track; this was the Duston Iron Co Ltd, controlled by Staveley Coal & Iron Co Ltd, Park Gate Iron Co Ltd and James Oakes & Co Ltd.

The tramway and stock were handed over by the Trustee's of Higgins' Estate and negotiations were put in hand with Earl Cowper's agent for the transfer of the lease; the board minutes of Staveley Coal & Iron Co Ltd for 28th May 1895 record a new lease in progress, but whether this was a renewal or for a fresh area is not specified. Ironstone quarrying was pursued vigorously both south and north of the Weedon road, and calcining was introduced in January 1891. Initially there were three faces on the southern side, one east of the main tramway and due north of the locomotive shed, and two east and west served by a branch that left the main tramway 300 yards west of the shed, at the northern end of the embankment. Horses are mentioned in the records, possibly for working the narrow gauge line. North of the A45, ore on the east of the main tramway was worked for one year only, when operations were transferred to the west, extending the previous working face of 1885 clockwise until it was parallel to, and about 100 yards from, Duston Road. Working here ceased in 1890 (possibly because of the increasing overburden) and from then onwards activity was confined to areas further west and south. The branch tramway referred to above was extended beneath the A45 in 1890 and quarrying pursued on both sides of the road, both anticlockwise. Working on the south finished in 1905 but on the north continued to 1908, the final face lying just inside the roadside hedge. The workings had also reached Mill Way, between the A45 and Duston village. The limestone quarry was worked for a short time only, and then abandoned, as the price required by the landowner was considered too high; the narrow gauge tramway was lifted and the 1901 OS merely shows the course of the line.

The lease was due to expire on 31st March 1908, by which time most of the available stone had been exhausted; an adjacent area would have yielded enough for a further eight year's work, but would have required another bridge (under Mill Way?). It was therefore decided to seek permission to work out what remained on the existing site in the six months allowed for the removal of plant, and then to dissolve the partnership as at 31st December 1908. Quarrying therefore presumably came to an end about September 1908.

Of the equipment used our main source of information from the pre-Duston Iron Ore Co Ltd days comes from the 1883 inventory and the associated legal correspondence connected with the purchase by the new company, all of which had gravitated to the Northamptonshire Record Office at Lamport Hall. Even the inventory has its limitations, though; it includes minutiae of stores down to bales of hay and a chaffcutter (? for horses working the narrow gauge line) and to cotton waste, oil and kindling

Duston Quarries. With its square tank and domeless boiler, Neilson 601 was a typical product of this builder at the time, 1861. She probably did most of the work in pre-Staveley days. In this posed picture she carried a card on the tank that appears to read 'Died at Duston October 1896'. An obituary note perhaps? (Mrs S. Baker)

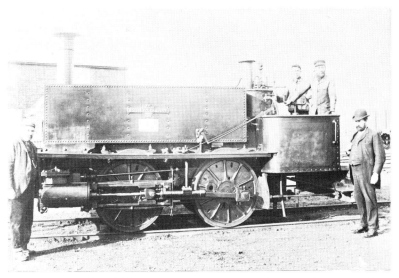

Duston Quarries. The Markham locomotive *DUSTON*was the usual performer during Staveley's occupation, and is here seen outside the locomotive shed, c 1900.

(Collection G. H. Starmer)

amongst the appurtenances of the 'locomotive shed with tiled roof', but no details of the rolling stock. However, we have some information on the locomotives. Some years before any archival material was discovered, ex-driver Baucutt told Bernard Roberts that they were 'Nelson with a square tank' and 'Brotherhood' which Bernard took to refer to the makers' names. Confirmation of the former came from the researches of Russell Wear into the records of Neilson & Co, in which spares are quoted as being supplied on 30th December 1874 to the Northamptonshire Iron Co, Duston Works, for locomotive No. 601. Then we have the fine photograph provided by Mrs. S. Baker of Burton Latimer, on which the number 601 can be read. The card carried by the locomotive bears the odd caption 'Died at Duston October 1896'; perhaps the engine was to be cut up and the photograph taken as a record, on return from Loddington. In 1866 George Pell's properties at Duston were offered for sale, Pell being under distress for rent; these properties included three locomotives—a 25hp (Neilson), a 2hp (sic—? 20hp) by Brotherhood and a 30hp 'locomotive and tender'—and ten railway wagons. The third engine is the only tender locomotive recorded as owned by an ironstone company, and we wish we knew more about it. 'Contract Journal' of 6th January 1909 carried an advertisement of a

Duston Quarries. Manning Wardle locomotive *PETERSTONE* approaches the LNWR junction, with behind her the canal bridge and the start of the 'high lines', the weakened state of which had forced the use of this lighter engine. c 1905.   (Collection G. H. Starmer)

Duston Quarries. *PETERSTONE* in the yard, c 1907. Note the different works plate, affixed after the rebuild by the makers in 1907.   (Collection G. H. Starmer)

locomotive for sale, with 11in. cylinders, presumably the Brotherhood.

The Staveley company purchased a new locomotive from Markham & Co for working the quarries; named *DUSTON*, she worked the traffic throughout, as there is no record until towards the end of operations of any spare engine other than the two old ones, which were probably little used. One was loaned to Loddington quarries for a short time in the middle 1890s. Because of the defective state of 'the viaduct' in the 1900s Staveley supplied a lighter engine, the Manning Wardle *PETERSTONE*, in exchange for *DUSTON*. *PETERSTONE* is recorded in the files of Markham & Co Ltd (extracted by Ken Plant) as being repaired at Duston in February 1906, but in 1907 she went to Manning Wardle's for a rebuild. What worked the quarry traffic in her absence is not known. On closure, *PETERSTONE* returned to Staveley works. The liveries of these two locomotives when at Duston is not recorded, but at Staveley *DUSTON* was painted black with red coupling rods.

After the closure track, plant and locomotives were removed, and the locomotive shed taken over by the lessor, but there was no restoration of the ground, and the course of the line and extent of the workings were very plainly in view up to World War II; some of the working faces were quite impressive, too, revealing a depth of ironstone considerably greater than average. But Duston was too near Northampton for this situation to continue and over the years most of the quarry landmarks have disappeared under housing and industrial development, and the main tramway route has been destroyed by gravel workings. The firm of F. E. Storton operated from a depot on Weedon Road, St. James's End, and in 1966 they were taken over by Mixconcrete Aggregates Ltd. By 1970 extensions to the workings towards Duston Mill resulted in the uprooting of hedges and bulldozing of the 'highlines', as the railway embankment was known locally. A few odd sections were left intact as the gravel quarrying operations went from east to west across the course of the tramway, but in general the area has been so disfigured as to make it difficult to pick out the few traces remaining.

Ground near the A45 was designated a 'Leisure Area' by Northampton Corporation, the level to be raised by tipping, thus obliterating the faces on the south side of the A45. This was in 1974, by which time Wilcon Construction Ltd were the owners of the area round the former locomotive shed; the latter was still standing but with a modern facade, and the stables and workmen's cottages derelict and due for demolition.

At the BR end, where the signal box had gone by 1966, there were no traces at all of the mineral line, though some sleepers remained on the canal

Duston Quarries. The layer of ironstone at Duston was reputed to be one of the thickest in the Midlands. The photograph shows the exposed face south of the Weedon road as it was in 1974. This site is now covered by factory development. ((G. H. Starmer)

bridge; but by 1977 these too had disappeared, and the surface of the bridge had been concreted. There are faint traces of the course of the line between canal and river, including some half-buried brickwork that probably supported the hefty timbers of the trestles. A pipeline spans the river just west of the old bridge site; and it should be mentioned, for the interest of ardent searchers for detail, that the course of the river is now different from that when the tramway was laid down! The former allotments bordering the south side of the A45 were being covered with rubble, as already mentioned, and there is no trace of the former bridges under the road; in 1979 the A45 was being doubled on this section, and some houses erected. On the north side industrial units are being built, and the ground surface contours altered to suit their requirements.

However, the areas further west and north were still in 1977 unaffected, and retain a deep face alongside Mill Way (from the A45 to Duston village) and a similar and perhaps even more striking working face runs parallel to Duston Road a hundred yards or so south of it. This face is about 25ft. deep and reveals the great thickness of ironstone that impressed the early quarrying operators. The limestone quarry was made into a static water reservoir in World War II by putting a concrete dam across the stream at the southern end. Of the limestone that crossed Duston Road in the vicinity of the junction with Bants Lane there is no trace. On the south side of the road there was a stone wall, in which there was a gap, protected by a gate, through which the tramway ran. This gap was still visible in 1970 but had disappeared by 1976, when the wall had been replaced by new fencing. All traces of the line north of Duston Road, visible up to World War II, were swept away by the construction of the large factory of British Timken Ltd; indeed it was stated that when the foundations of the factory were being laid, the pile driver encountered some resistance that proved to be the ironwork of some wagons that had evidently been abandoned on the site half a century before. There is still a flooded depression (used as an oil sump) inside the factory boundary fence, visible from the playing fields at the back of Mendip Road, which is almost certainly part of the old quarry site; not that it looks much like it in its present guise. No; the best place to look at is the deep ironstone face near Duston Road — that **is** worth seeing, while it lasts.

Grid References

732595	Junction with LNWR
731596	Bridge over canal
738606	Locomotive shed
732607	Bridge under A45, Weedon
728611	Level crossing of Duston road
724607	Mill Way roadside face (north end)
726615	Old limestone quarry, near pond/sump

Locomotives

Gauge; 4ft. 8½in.

-	Tender locomotive, details unknown								S/S c 1866
-	0-4-0ST	OC	N	601	1861	10x18in(?)		(a)	Scr
-	0-4-0ST	OC	Brotherhood			11 x in.			Scr c 1909
DUSTON	0-4-0ST	OC	Mkm	103	1891	12 x 20in.	3ft. 6in.	New 7/1891 (1)	
PETERSTONE	0-4-0ST	OC	MW	1023	1887	12 x 18in.	3ft.0in.	(b) (2)	

(a) formerly Glasgow Iron Co.
(b) ex Staveley Ironworks c 1905.

(1) to Staveley Works c 1906
(2) to Staveley Works 1909

One locomotive loaned to Loddington Ironstone Co Ltd 11/1894 to 10/1896; this was probably N 601.

HUNSBURY HILL QUARRIES

Owners: Northampton Coal, Iron & Wagon Co: Hunsbury Hill Coal & Iron Co Ltd from 1876: Hunsbury Hill Iron Co from 1883: P. Phipps from 23rd February 1889: P. Phipps Executors: Hunsbury Hill Iron Co from c.1922: Richard Thomas & Co Ltd from September 1935.

The presence of outcrops of iron ore at Hunsbury Hill was recognised about 1857 or possibly earlier, but it was not until 1873 that they were developed, in association with the erection of Hunsbury Ironworks (*Northampton Mercury*, 30th August 1873 and other issues). MS quotes both works and quarries in production in that year and F. Whellan (*History of Northamptonshire*, 1874, p.262) states that 'ironstone is extensively worked at Hunsbury Hill and two furnaces are in course of erection'. Initially the furnaces were fed with ore from their immediate vicinity; as however most of the ore was concentrated on the upper slopes of the hill, it soon became necessary to develop these deposits, and small workings southeast of Rothersthorpe Road were opened in the late 1870s, and a mineral line of 3ft. 8in. gauge was laid between them and the furnaces, while traffic from the latter was handled by standard gauge locomotives.

The tramway was closed in 1921, long before interest in industrial tramways embraced more than a handful of enthusiasts; while the few such individuals who came later to pick up the history of this bygone line were faced with the proximity of Northampton, which swallowed up in its anonymity most of the former personnel, that in a rural community would have been more readily identifiable. These two factors however had a happy outcome when the Rushden Railway Society had the idea of reviving a former ironstone line as part of the railway preservation movement. The early demise of the ironworks and its associated tramway meant that there was no restoration of the route to agriculture; and the Northampton Development Corporation were able and willing to give financial support to the scheme. As a result, while many elements of the early history are imperfectly known, physical details of its route and appearance are to be seen today... and for many years to come, we hope.

Practically the whole of the quarried area was on ground belonging to the Bouverie family, whose Delapre estate in the mid-nineteenth century embraced the Hunsbury Hill area, Delapre Abbey and Park, and much of the village of Hardingstone. The Richard Thomas & Baldwin files at Corby record that the purchase by the Northampton Coal, Iron & Wagon Co of the 12-acre works site was completed on 10th December 1873, while the

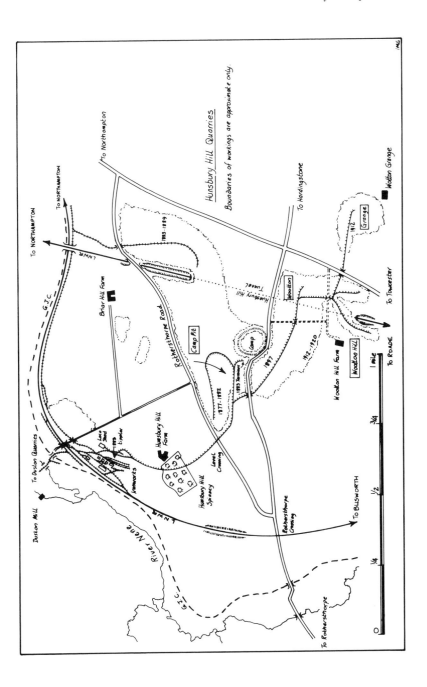

Hunsbury Hill Farm lease of 170 acres lay south of the works, bounded by the LNWR Blisworth line to the west, the 'Green Lane' (see later) to the south and the line of hedges eastwards by the acquisiton from the Bouverie Estate of the Briar Hill Farm lease of 143 acres, lying between the Blisworth line (to the north), the LNWR Northampton-Roade line (to the east) and Rothersthorpe Road (to the south).

For most of its productive life the Hunsbury ironworks was in the possession of the Phipps family, who also owned the well-known Northampton brewery, and their control commenced in August 1877, one year after the formation of the Hunsbury Hill Coal & Iron Co Ltd, so that the various changes in title are largely nominal. Ironstone working was actively pursued on the Hunsbury Hill Farm site, up to the edge of Briar Hill Farm, but not extended thereon. About 1883 Pickering Phipps III purchased Hunsbury Hill Farm, while for many years barley for use in the brewery was grown on Briar Hill Farm. It was at this time that quarrying operations were extended to the area around the ancient earthwork of Danes Camp; this was scheduled as an Ancient Monument under an 1882 Act, and was not included in the lease, but there were numerous archaeological finds in the surrounding area. Pickering Phipps, the company chairman, took a sympathetic interest and rewarded all workmen making finds, so that archaeologists benefited by the (at that time) most thorough excavation accorded to a site of this kind. In the period of excavation for ironstone, 1882-87, over three hundred articles were discovered, including iron weapons, implements and remains of slag that indicated the smelting of iron in bygone centuries (*Victoria County History of Northamptonshire*, Vol 1, p.152).

At Danes Camp (usually shortened to 'Camp Pit') the stone was at first worked as outcrop, but then under increasing cover, and when the pit was approaching exhaustion a further and much larger area was acquired; known as the Wootton lease, this covered 710 acres and extended eastwards from the Grand Union Canal, bounded by 'Green Lane' (Mere Way) on the north, and the stream to the south, as far as the Northampton-Stony Stratford road, but excluding Wootton Hall and grounds in the northeast corner. The Towcester road crossed the property and so did the LNWR line to Roade as it emerged from the tunnel; to the west lay Wootton Hill Farm, while Wootton Grange lay at about the centre of the leased area. The tramway was extended to cross 'Green Lane' immediately west of Danes Camp, and the Wootton Hill pit was opened up by 1897; working edged eastwards, the tramway being taken under the Towcester road by a tunnel driven in 1912[1]. The final workings were in the vicinity of Wootton

Grange, and the area east of the Grange was never touched. Overburden in the Wootton pit reached about 18ft.

Having briefly described the quarrying areas, we can now look at the tramway serving them. The tramway left the works in a south south westerly direction on an embankment trending obliquely up the hillside to the northern edge of Hunsbury Hill spinney, where it curved fairly sharply to the south south east towards Rothersthorpe Road ('Banbury Lane' on old maps, this being a drover's road of considerable antiquity) along the flank of the hill but climbing steadily; there was a stiff bank in the spinney (in shallow cutting at the southern side) and another cutting near the road, which was crossed on the level. Between here and the 'Green Lane' to the south is Danes Camp and the surrounding area is known as 'the Old Mere', while the 'Green Lane' is called Mere Way. The Wootton quarries were served by a branch that crossed Mere Way and from there on was in cutting that became progressively deeper as it followed the ironstone bed beneath rising ground, over the tunnel occupied by the LNWR Northampton-Roade line, and then beneath the Towcester road via a low tunnel to the most distant workings near Wootton Grange. On this section were two bridges under farm tracks, that near the A43 being a substantial one with brick abutments and wooden fencing.

Sam Warwick, who started work as a 'horse boy' at Hunsbury Hill about 1904 at the age of fifteen recalled[2] the hard work of those days, which was from 6.0am to 5.0pm. there were no holidays; no work (and no pay) on wet days; no pensions; no sick pay; compensation for injury sometimes but not always; the sack or suspension for offences. His wages were of the order of six shillings per week when he started; later, when in charge of the calcine bank, he received 24 shillings per week. All the quarry work was manual; the overburden was removed by pick and shovel and carried away by the familiar barrow and plank method, and the ironstone was loaded into the wagons by long iron forks, with larger pieces by hand. A photograph shows that the wagons were filled well over the boards. When full, the loaded wagons were pulled up the gradient out of the pit by horse in the charge of a 'horse boy'; the wagons were then allowed to run in pairs by gravity across Hunsbury Hill to the works, under the charge of a brakesman riding on the 'bumper', the brake being operated by foot. At the furnace end the wagons were weighed and emptied, and the contents put on the calcine bank; the normal furnace charge consisted of equal volumes of raw and calcined ore, the raw ironstone coming from other pits (presumably Blisworth) owned by the company. At one time there was a weigh hut on 'The Mere' but the use of this was discontinued before Mr. Warwick's day. The empty tubs were

Hunsbury Hill Quarries. A posed photograph of a wagon team at Green Lane crossing, 1900, showing loaded and empty wagons, horses, drivers and brakesmen.

(Northamptonshire Ironstone Railway Trust)

Hunsbury Hill Quarries. Official photograph of *NORTHAMPTON*, the first of the set of three locomotives (Bagnall 1955-57) supplied new in 1912 to work the main quarry system. They were of restricted height to negotiate the tunnel under the Towcester road. Unfortunately no photographs of the locomotives at work seem to have survived.

(Smyth Collection)

hauled back to the pits by horses; these animals were mostly obtained from the brewery when they were too old to haul the heavy drays.

The wagons were of wood and were built at the ironworks; the castings were made at the works but axles were bought in. They had a block of wood about 9in. thick as a buffer ('bumper') and were fitted with an iron rod as a tipping lever. The content was about fifteen hundredweight of ore; some larger wagons were introduced but proved to be too heavy for tipping. The terminus of the narrow gauge tramway is shown on the 1883 OS at right angles to a standard gauge siding at the ironworks, clearly suggesting that the wagons were end-tippers. However this system was superseded by the use of side-tippers, as shown in the photograph at 'Green Lane' taken about 1900; possibly this was in connection with calcining.

In 1912 three locomotives were obtained from W. G. Bagnall Ltd to the tramway's original gauge of 3ft. 8in., and reduced clearance (8ft. 5in. from rail level) to pass the small bore of the tunnel under the Towcester road. At this time the wagons were of the same general pattern as used at Lamport and Kettering, and overall dimensions of examples measured at Finedon were 3ft. 2in. across the frames, with bodies 6ft. 10in. by 6ft. 10in. by 3ft. 0in. high, and with a total length of 9ft. 2in. The layout at the ironworks had been modified to suit the side-tipping wagons and now a brick shed for the locomotives was built at the end of the narrow gauge track. Operation of the tramway was then much simpler; the locomotive took the empty wagons to the working face and returned with a rake already filled, which was emptied at the ironworks.

It is believed that Pickering Phipps intended to develop the ironstone reserves on Briar Hill Farm in the early years of the century. Finally, there was a standard gauge line to pits east of the tunnel over the LNWR line to Roade, presumably worked by an ironworks locomotive in the early 1880s.

World War I was a time of crisis for Hunsbury ironworks; the furnaces were damped down in October 1915 because of the 'unsatisfactory state of the pig-iron market'[3], though the depletion of iron ore reserves and call up of employees for the armed forces were also suggested as possible reasons. However, under orders from the Ministry of Munitions, the furnaces were relit in June 1917, and former employees were released from the forces. The chairman was keen to keep the works in production and to this end propounded an ambitious scheme to extend the quarrying area eastwards along the high ground south of Hardingstone and beyond; with the tramway being operated by locomotives there would be no serious transport problems and in obtaining the ground Phipps had a close ally in Delapre Estates, who owned most of the relevant land. Two plots vital to

Hunsbury Hill Quarries. Bridge carrying a farm track over the tramway west of the A43. The bridge has now gone and the area much altered.

(G. H. Starmer)

Hunsbury Hill Quarries. The embanked trackbed of the narrow gauge tramway as it approached the ironworks site (by then occupied by John Blackwood Hodge & Co Ltd), after emerging from Hunsbury Hill Spinney (see photo in Part I). 27th April 1963. (S. A. Leleux)

the scheme were glebe land owned by the church at Hardingstone, and Delapre Estates purchased these in 1918 to facilitate Phipp's scheme; and in that year Phipps obtained a ten-year lease to work ironstone on much of the necessary land at Hardingstone. These included fields south of the A50, i.e. the other side of the road from the very early 'Quarry fields' described under the Hardingstone Quarries section. In the event of course the quarries were never extended to these limits, and indeed did not even reach the limit of

Hunsbury Hill Quarries. Tunnel under Towcester Road, looking southeast, 15th May 1965. This area has been much altered by building and road alterations, but the bridge parapets remained in 1987. (S. A. Leleux)

113

the Wootton lease, as the end of the war put a vastly different complexion on matters; demand fell off sharply and the plant needed a fair amount of renewal. Pickering Phipps was still anxious to go ahead with his scheme of expansion but was overruled by other directors, who preferred to confine the family fortunes to the more profitable concern of brewing. The furnaces were blown out 28th January 1921; even so, Pickering Phipps intended to reopen the works as soon as trade improved, but he died a short time after the closure.

Richard Thomas & Co Ltd acquired the ironworks (which had remained derelict, complete with most of the equipment, locomotives, tramways and all since 1921) in September 1935, along with the associated land, freehold and leasehold; this included the Hunsbury Hill Farm area (170 acres) owned by Phipps, the Briar Hill Farm area (143 acres) owned by Delapre Estates, and the Wootton area (710 acres). The last two leased areas were for 27 years from 29th September 1935. The small area south of the A50 at Hardingstone, leased by Phipps in 1918, was not taken up by Richard Thomas however. The odd period of 27 years suggests that possibly it was the unexpired portion of a lease allotted to the Hunsbury Iron Co.

The 'takeover' by Richard Thomas did not appear to alter matters very much, and hopes that the ironworks might be reopened soon dwindled as the months of idleness lengthened, and eventually the works were demolished. Richard Thomas had intentions of reopening the quarries, however, and at a meeting with the consulting engineering firm of H. A. Brassert & Co held at Irthlingborough 8th June 1937 to discuss the development of their newly acquired Northamptonshire properties it was revealed that their application for the reinstatement of the level crossing of the ironstone tramway with the Rothersthorpe Road had been refused by the local authority, but that they were considering an application to the Ministry of Transport for such permission. To work the quarries they proposed using the temporary plant (a diesel digger and a steam transporter) released from the reopened Finedon (Buccleuch) quarries when the larger machines for the latter were delivered. These smaller machines would be used at Danes Camp and possibly on Briar Hill also 'if it is desired to open up this property to assist production'.[4]

There was no reopening however and the company concentrated their attentions on the Finedon area, for this purpose taking narrow gauge rails, locomotive *WOOTTON* and some twenty wagons from Hunsbury Hill for opening up the Buccleuch site. It is not clear whether the whole of the narrow gauge tramway was lifted at this period, but it seems likely, as some of it must have been taken up; and two standard gauge locomotives were

Hunsbury Hill Quarries. The furthest workings were at Wootton Grange, and the photograph shows how they appeared on 29th July 1966. The area has now been built on. (G. H. Starmer)

115

cut up about the same time, suggesting a clearing-up operation. However, the rest of the locomotives were left until 1940/1; the last in service, possibly on clearance work, was *WHISTON*, which was transferred to Finedon quarries. It was a pity that none of the Bagnalls survived to the post World War II period, when they could have been noted and photographed by the then much greater number of people interested in industrial railways. They had done less than ten years work and were of an unusual design; but it was not to be.

The ironworks site was acquired by the engineering firm of John Blackwood, Hodge & Co Ltd, the surviving buildings were modified to their requirements and new ones were added. Richard Thomas & Baldwins Ltd (who had succeeded Richard Thomas & Co Ltd in 1945) were still considering reopening the quarries; a report dated 18th June 1952 by T. W. F. Spencer to RTB[4] states that ore could be loaded into road vehicles and conveyed 1200 yards to a loading site in Hunsbury Works yard, as in the sale to Blackwood Hodge they had reserved siding rights. Further, according to Mr. Ansell, Agent for Delapre Estates, the Wootton lease was extended to 29th September 1977; but again, nothing practical transpired, and RTB later said that the ore at Hardingstone (presumably the Wootton area) was of uncertain quality and that they did not intend to work it, despite the lease.

Thus, at the Hunsbury Hill Ironworks site, the remains of the narrow gauge, always on the perimeter of operations, were unaffected and were allowed to return to nature unhampered, and the locomotive shed was converted into a workshop and store. The embankment remained in position but at the western end was a bridge where it crossed an accommodation road for farm vehicles, and this bridge was removed. The route through Hunsbury Hill spinney and across the fields was easily traceable, though somewhat overgrown, and the crossing of Rothersthorpe Road was marked by a slight ledge in the otherwise smooth slope of the road. The fields towards the ironworks were sunk below road level where ore had been extracted. South of the road the most prominent traces were the final gullet of a roughly circular quarry near Danes Camp, but these too were filled with undergrowth, as was also the course further south towards the Towcester road. The cutting here was steep-sided and on either hand could be seen the ventilation shafts of the BR tunnel. The bridge under the A43 (Northampton-Towcester) was marked by fairly ornate parapets, the main walls of red brick with a layer of blue bricks near ground level and a layer of larger blue bricks at the top, the whole between pillars surmounted by tetrahedral concrete slabs. Inevitably some vandalism had occurred but the parapets were largely intact, though the bridge had been filled in beneath.

Towards Wootton Grange the course was clear but overgrown, and covered at one point by the earthworks of a gas pipeline. Traces of a trailing junction to the working face could be seen and the ground was below road level.

Like Duston, these remains would in the ordinary course of events have been engulfed in the enlarging Northampton, and indeed new roads have obliterated sections between Rothersthorpe Road and the ironworks site. However, as stated above, other sections have been saved by the preservation movement, though the origins of this were indirect, as is so often the case. The Rushden Railway Society was formed in December 1971 with the intentions of purchasing and restoring *No. 87* (and also *No. 86* if possible) that had been lying in local yards since the closure of the Wellingborough Iron Co's metre gauge line five years earlier: providing a building to house these and other relics from the Northamptonshire ironstone quarries: and running the locomotive(s) from time to time on rails laid on a former local BR line or ironstone quarry trackbed. Realisation of these aims was hampered by the smallness of the Society, who concentrated their efforts on the restoration of *No. 87*; but the turning point came with the idea of utilizing part of the course of the Hunsbury Hill tramway, that had by then come to the notice of Northampton Development Corporation. This body, in partnership with Northampton County Borough Council, had been made responsible for enlarging the city to house eventually a further 100,000 people. A master plan published by the NDC in 1968 included a major residential area built around the slopes of Hunsbury Hill, with the Iron Age hill fort of Danes Camp in the centre; and in the planning proposals was the comment 'The Development Corporation proposes to retain the disused ironstone railway system... this will create an opportunity of reinstating a rare narrow gauge track as an element of real interest in the park. It may be possible to establish a museum related to the ironstone workings, the railway and Danes Camp'. The proposals complemented nicely the activities of the Rushden Railway Society, which was re-formed in June 1973 under the style of the Northamptonshire Ironstone Railway Trust Ltd. The NIRT was much better fitted to attract members and get things done, and gradually plans were matured. In February 1975 the Trust was given access to a small area near Green Lane (Mere Way) to assemble items that had already been acquired. The former railway site and land were made available to the Trust on 1st October 1975 by the NDC and the affected tenant, Mr. Rose. Work then began in earnest in clearing the site, laying track and generally preparing for the arrival of exhibits.

The Trust lost no time in constructing and filling a temporary compound on the site bordering Green Lane, commencing with stock obtained direct from industry; these included the two Pecketts *Nos. 86* and *87,* but the first locomotive on the Hunsbury Hill scene in the widest sense was a standard gauge diesel donated by a firm near Norwich and which Blackwood Hodge kindly accommodated on a length of track outside the former narrow gauge shed. The NIRT was unfortunate in being formed too late to acquire much material direct from the ironstone quarrying industry, as by 1974 the heavy programme of contraction which had closed thirty systems in fifteen years had ended; in this period many locomotives in particular were given or sold at nominal sums to many preservation bodies all over the country. As a result, none of the stock in the possession of the NIRT, except for the Pecketts, had any direct connection with ironstone, though most of the items had associations with the county. However, by the autumn of 1975, they were able to put into execution plans for laying track and generally open up the site, with the hope always before them of obtaining genuine ironstone exhibits secondhand. One of the first tasks was to clear selected parts of the route of half a century's growth; this included the irregular 'circular' formation near Danes Camp, which it was intended to relay with metre gauge track. In clearing away the undergrowth, a section of the

Hunsbury Hill Quarries. Trackbed of ironstone line with Danes Camp in the background, 27th April 1963. This route was laid with track by the N.I.R.T., first with metre gauge (1976) and then with standard gauge (1982). (S. A. Leleux)

Hunsbury Hill Quarries. During the course of clearing the circular route for the installation of metre gauge track, some of the original 3ft. 8in. gauge track was uncovered, and is being examined here by members of the photographer's family. 1st August 1976.

(S. A. Leleux)

original 3ft. 8in. track was exposed, and one is tempted to go back 90 years when, almost on the same spot, quarriers at Danes Camp were unearthing exhibits of interest to the archaeologists of the day. The cutting south of Green Lane was exposed by a bulldozer, excavator and a lot of manual labour, for a considerable distance. Between Rothersthorpe Road and Danes Camp some mixed standard and metre gauge track was laid in late 1975, and a new headquarters was established, including a compound to which the material in the temporary compound was later moved. There was also a 2ft. gauge line laid on the south side of Green Lane opposite the original compound; this was in April 1976.

The NIRT had moved in none too soon. Urban roadway extension in the vicinity of Rothersthorpe road had, in the blanketing manner of modern earth-moving machinery, obliterated some traces of the former tramway; Briar Hill Farm is now a housing estate, while Hunsbury Hill Farm was still owned by the British Steel Corporation, as successors to Richard Thomas & Baldwins Ltd. Sadly, the later 1970s did not maintain the promise of the formative years. The 2ft. line was not operated after the one season and rapidly became overgrown; the Danes Camp loop was cleared again — but very slowly and by 1979 the trackbed was far from complete, so that there was little to interest the casual visitor. On the other hand, a locomotive and

119

wagon formerly at Irchester quarries were acquired. This trend was reversed in the 1980s; the NDC were completing their road-building programme in the vicinity, and provided the Trust with fresh capital, enabling them to go ahead with a revised and more ambitious scheme. By the end of 1982 the circular layout was complete, but using standard gauge, with the locomotives and other exhibits on a central site; a branch from this was laid across Green Lane and extended towards the Towcester road. These new plans gave a layout more attractive to the general public at the expense of a further departure from the concept of retaining as much as possible of the original Hunsbury Hill system.

Indeed, it is true to say that the more interesting remains of the Hunsbury Hill tramway are outside the Country Park rather than in it. At the rear of the new church can be seen the trackbed in a shallow cutting between hedges, traceable across the road below; across the field beyond the course can be made out, and there is a very strongly marked cutting through Hunsbury Hill spinney (now designated a nature reserve) with its steel slope downwards to the bend at the bottom; how the horses must have panted and the Bagnalls barked, climbing through the spinney! Below the latter lies the new double road, with the trackbed continued on an embankment among trees on the other side to the rear of Blackwood Hodge's works, where the former narrow gauge locomotive shed still remains (1982). At the other end of the system the cutting towards the Wootton pit is on the fringe of the Park and the 1975 clearance had turned the trackbed into an unofficial footpath along which we can stroll and in imagination relive bygone days. The ironstone face is very well marked on the north side, and towards the former Towcester Road bridge the route is waterlogged and filled with bulrushes. The bridge under the A43 road still (1987) survives with its parapets, but is difficult to find in the complete regorganization of the road layout, while the route to the Wootton pit beyond is under urban redevelopment — but we must be thankful for the sites that have been preserved for us.

Footnotes

1.   Agreement with Northamptonshire County Council, 11th January 1912.
2.   Northamptonshire Ironstone Railway Trust, Newsletter, February 1977.
3.   *Banbury Guardian*, 17th May 1917.
4.   From correspondence files held by Mr. A. J. Pack, former surveyor to RTB, to whom I am indebted for permission to inspect them.

Grid References

732593	Tipping dock from ng (second site)
731578	Cutting through Hunsbury Hill spinney (south end)
732593	Locomotive shed
732586	Level crossing with Rothersthorpe road
742578	Bridge under Towcester road
743577	Terminus of Wootton pit

Locomotives

Gauge; 3ft. 8in.

HARDINGSTONE	0-6-0ST	OC	WB	1955	1912	13 x 18in.	2ft.9¼in.	New 9/1912	Scr 1940
WOOTTON	0-6-0ST	OC	WB	1956	1912	13 x 18in.	2ft.9¼in.	New 11/1912	(1)
NORTHAMPTON	0-6-0ST	OC	WB	1957	1912	13 x 18in.	2ft.9¼in.	New 12/1912	Scr 1940

(1) to Richard Thomas & Co Ltd, Finedon Quarries, 1937

HARDINGSTONE QUARRIES

Owners: S. H. Blackwell & Co.

At the present state of our knowledge these were among the earliest East Midlands ironstone quarries of the Victorian era to be worked on a commercial basis; and they had a tramway connection to a mainline. Though shortlived, it was therefore a system worthy of special note, which it did not get in *IRTM*—in fact it was not mentioned at all! The site is not referred to in MS, and the only printed references in geological works known to us are an undated one in GSM to 'early workings at Hardingstone' and a note in NSI 'small workings were operated southeast of Hardingstone between 1870 and 1880'. Credit for the discovery of these quarries goes wholly to Fred Dix, and the historical importance of the site warrants a note on the circumstances that brought it to light.

The *Northampton Mercury and Herald* of 30th April 1970 was its 250th anniversary issue, and one of the articles contained reminiscences of a Mr. Ansell, aged 82, a resident of Hardingstone and manager of the Bouverie Estate since 1916. The Bouverie Estate at one time was very extensive, including Delapre (the family lived at Delapre Abbey), Hunsbury Hill and most of the land about Hardingstone, and Mr. Ansell stated that as a lad he was told that ironstone had been extracted from land that was in 1970 part of Pittams' Farm at Hardingstone. Mr. Dix read this and wrote to Mr. Ansell, who kindly offered to show him the site where traces of the quarry were to be seen and even clearer indications of a tramway connection to the LNWR Blisworth-Peterborough line, about a mile away. Mr. Ansell did not know the date of operations, nor the name of the owners, but he thought it was probably Butlins. However, Mr. Dix then contacted Mr. P. A. King, Archivist to the Northamptonshire Record Office (by a coincidence, then at Delapre Abbey) and was invited by him to inspect the Bouverie Estate documents, which included an Indenture dated 25th September 1852 between Edward Bouverie and 'Samuel Holden Blackwell of Dudley, Worcestershire (Ironmaster) and Samuel Wagstaff Smith of Northampton (Gentleman)' permitting the latter partnership to take ironstone from the land known as Woodway Close and Great Warren. Thus the bare bones of the history, which we will now clothe with such material as can be gleaned from the contemporary press and recent inspection of the site.

The Indenture states that the agreement should be effective from 25th March 1852, presumably indicating that some extraction of ore had already been carried out as an experiment but was now being placed on a

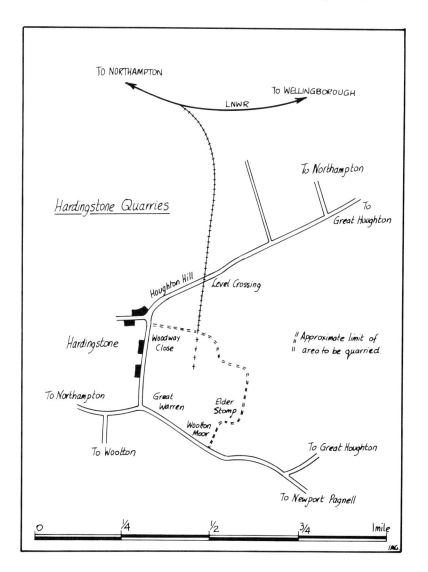

commercial basis; leases are very often retrospective. The *Northampton Mercury* for the first six months of 1852 contains several references to 'Northamptonshire Iron Ore', the most significant being an extract from the half-yearly meeting of the LNWR, at which a Mr. Glyn stated that 'we have also had in the last half year a curious fact developed which certainly would add materially to our local traffic; namely, the discovery (and it is curious that, in these days, it should have been a discovery) of a very large mineral district in the middle of Northamptonshire. Ironstone has been discovered there in great quantities, and the want of this article in South Staffordshire is so great that it will certainly lead to a very considerable traffic from one place to the other'. This appears in the issue of 28th February 1852, and though the precise sources of the traffic are not stated, they may be presumed to include the Hardingstone, Gayton and Irthlingborough areas, which seem to have been in course of development at the same time.

S. H. Blackwell, who was the proprietor of furnaces at Russells Hall, Dudley and at Bilston ('New Furnaces') himself wrote a long letter to the *Northampton Mercury*, published in their issue of 13th March 1852, and including the statement 'As the party most immediately concerned in the introduction of mining operations into Northamptonshire ... it will give me great pleasure if I should become permanently connected with your town'; and in the course of a lecture on 7th April 1852 to the British Iron Trades Association on *Iron Mining Resources in the United Kingdom* he says '... it (the Northampton ore) appears to be developed most largely, and to be of the best quality, along the Northampton-Peterborough line of railway from Higham Ferrers to Hardingstone, near Northampton, and again from Gayton, near Blisworth, to Towcester'.

Even before this, some quarrying was in progress, and again we look to the '*Northampton Mercury*' for a report in their issue of 24th January 1852; 'We understand that a single ironmaster in the neighbourhood of Dudley is conveying away the ironstone of this county at the rate of 200 tons per week. The firm in question is making a railway siding at Northampton Station for the express purpose of facilitating conveyance. An excellent vein has been opened at Wootton, the property of Mr. Evans, at the back of the workhouse'. Quite apart from the importance of this as the first printed reference to the commercial usage of East Midlands iron ore that has come to light, the report gives rise to some interesting speculations. The ironmaster could well have been S. H. Blackwell; and the site is only a few hundred yards from the Hardingstone 'Quarry Fields' but on the south side of the road. It seems probable that the ore was carried by cart to Northampton Station (presumably Bridge St.).

Putting these together, it seems probable that Blackwell started Wootton quarry, in a big enough way to warrant establishment of a railway siding to handle the output, and then moved to the other side of the road, where the ore was perhaps of better quality. It would be very interesting to learn the circumstances of the discovery at Wootton. Finally, it seems practically certain that operations must have commenced at Wootton in 1851—which could make it the first commercial ironstone quarry in the East Midlands.

Turning now to the Hardingstone quarries proper, the lease was for some 36 acres of land under the name of Woodway Close and Great Warren, at the time occupied or tenanted by Thomas Timms Bartlams; and Pennylands (27 acres) and parts of Wootton Moor and Elder Stamp (7 acres) worked by Francis and Thomas Underwood. Francis Underwood was the grandfather of Mrs. Pittams, the wife of the owner (in 1970) of 'the Farm' at Hardingstone, and Mr. Ansell has an account book including an item for the payment of rent in 1882 by Francis Underwood for 'the Quarry Fields'. Only ironstone was to be extracted, and the right of way given for the building of engine houses, tramways, bridges and a railway to the Railway Company; but no smelting was to be carried out. The royalty was 9d. per ton of the traditional 22 hundredweight—a high figure; and the minimum royalty payable was £400 per annum, plus an annual rent of £3 per acre. An unusual provision was that no more than two excavations at any one time were permitted—an early example of amenity preservation! A plan attached to the lease shows a proposed rail connection to the LNWR, making a junction facing Northampton.

The workings were known as the 'Warren Quarries'; and the 'Quarry Fields' lie between the Newport Pagnell road (B526) on the south and the vicinity of the farm. A bridleway runs across them, from the farmyard to the B526, and on each side of this the ground is at a slightly lower level; the main quarrying area on the south side is a field that still possesses undulations suggestive of one-time disturbance, though obviously cultivation for more than a century has done much to resettle the land. To the north of the bridleway the land drops away and the tramway ran in a north easterly direction down the slopes of a valley towards the road at the bottom of Houghton Hill; Mr Underwood supplied this information, which had been passed on to Mrs. Pittams, his granddaughter. Mrs. Pittams also said that in years gone by ploughing had revealed traces of railway lines in the quarried area, but in the valley itself it is difficult to pick out any sort of route. However, north of the road to Houghton, are quite unmistakable traces of a shallow embankment running alongside a hedge in the direction of the LNWR line; near Home Farm the route became progressively less well-defined in the flat ground and in 1975 a new motorway obliterated all traces at the northern end.

As to tramway operation there is no information whatsoever. The total distance, about a mile, would make a locomotive useful but not essential. The low level remains suggest a standard gauge line, but whether this was continued up the hillside seems doubtful; in any case, cable haulage would be required (hence perhaps the reference to 'engine house' in the lease). A narrow gauge system in the quarry with transhipment at the top or bottom of the incline is possible; with perhaps horses working this and either horse or locomotive working the standard gauge section. We just do not know, and can only guess until and unless further information comes to light.

As said, the quarries are not mentioned in MS, so that we are pretty safe in assuming that they did not operate for very long, maybe only a few years. Blackwell, for all his lectures and letters, was secretive about the precise scene of his operations, possibly for commercial reasons, and did not inform Robert Hunt of them. Even so, it seems doubtful if they could have reached the 1860s unnoticed — but the traces are there to be seen today. The above-mentioned note in NSI to 'workings .. between 1870 and 1880' is hard to explain in the absence of any reference in MS; the Deposited Plans of the Bedford & Northampton Railway dated November 1865 show no tramway

Hardingstone Quarries. Raised course of standard gauge trackbed towards the LNWR line. Hardingstone Power Station is in left background. 2nd December 1976. (Eric Tonks)

connections, nor does there appear to be a record of the siding in LNWR files. In view of the mysteries still surrounding this location we cannot be dogmatic on this point and will leave the matter open in the hope that further information may come to light.

Grid Reference

769593	Junction with LNWR.
770581	Level crossing.
769578	Top of incline.
771570	South east corner of quarry.

EASTERN GROUP

East of Northampton, between there and Wellingborough, lay a small group of quarries on the high ground overlooking the Nene; these comprised another very early system dating from the 1850s and two shortlived ones from World War I. While none were of much consequence in terms of output, they form an interesting group; Cogenhoe pursued mining as well as quarrying, Earls Barton used an aerial ropeway to take the ore to the railway, and Whiston had four owners in eight years!

COGENHOE QUARRIES AND MINES

Owners: Cogenhoe Iron Ore Co; Exors of Edward Saunders from 1877; Cogenhoe Iron Ore Co from 1880; F. Cohen from 1886.

Operations commenced at Cogenhoe as early as 1858, and in the following year both opencast and mining methods were in use at 'The Firs', a patch of woodland on the summit of the ridge southeast of the village; a narrow gauge rope-worked incline ran down to a point just south of the road to Grendon, where there was a tipping dock to a standard gauge line connecting with the LNWR Northampton-Peterborough line between Billing and Castle Ashby stations. There is a reference to the mines in *Mining Journal* for 1859, p.814, under 'Cooknoe' (sic), but these were short-lived, the bulk of the stone being got opencast. *Mining Journal* for 14th March 1868, p.194 refers to mines 'about to be opened out' and the issue of 18th May 1870, p.457, mentions 'new fields just opened at Cogenhoe'. About this time the standard gauge line was extended from its early terminus just south of the level crossing along the little valley to a point south of Cogenhoe school, where a considerable area of outcropping stone was quarried and again conveyed to the standard gauge by narrow gauge tramway; a cable-worked incline was not necessary in this case, the full tubs being allowed to run down most of the way by gravity. At the foot of the slope the tramway ran on to a wooden platform over the standard gauge line and the ore was tipped into the wagons below. Horses were used to haul the empty tubs back, about twelve at a time, and they were trained to push full ones with their shoulder on to the platform. The gauge of the quarry tramways is said to have been about 2ft., and the wooden 'dolly tubs' to hold about 8 cwt of ore, an unusually small quantity.

Edward Saunders was the manager for many years, and presumably the proprietor, as from 1877 to 1879 the ownership is credited to his executors. The *Northampton Mercury* of 17th April 1880 (thanks to Geoffrey Starmer for this) records that the concern had been sold under Sheriff's Warrant. MS for 1880 records the owners as Cogenhoe Iron Co again, but presumably under new ownership. Walter Burke had been foreman under Saunders, and probably took over, as he left in 1886 to take over ironstone quarries at Caythorpe in Lincolnshire. The later manager at Cogenhoe, Cohen, also had some connections with Caythorpe. Incidentally, he sustained serious injury from one of the engines at Cogenhoe.

It seems that the company was in some difficulty at this time. In 1886 F. Cohen is recorded in MS as owning the quarries, but in *The Engineer* of 11th November 1887 appeared the advertisement — 'For sale — Blast Furnaces, ironstone pits at Cogenhoe with plant including 100 10-ton wagons and two locomotives. F. Cohen, Grantham'. The 'Grantham' is explained by Cohen's involvement at Caythorpe, but the reference to blast furnaces is a mystery; he may have owned some in Nottinghamshire.

At first horses were used for haulage on the standard gauge line but later were displaced by two secondhand steam locomotives that were housed in a shed near the level crossing. One of these is said to have been named *ALATHEA CHOICE*, a title remembered for its strangeness and because the lady herself pursued an illicit romance with the engine driver, Tom Jeffs; the other engine was named after a lady too, it was said, but it seems that she was too respectable to be worth remembering!

The identities of these locomotives were for long a mystery, but have now been established beyond any reasonable doubt by the researches of the late S. H. Pearce Higgins (*Industrial Railway Record*, Vol 3, p.177; and private correspondence). The first clue came from the announcement by Thomas Merry, auctioneers of Northampton, when they offered (by order of **Mrs.** F. Cohen) the equipment on closure; this was on 16th July 1888 and the locomotives were described as 'a large loco built by Stephenson & Co and a smaller ditto by Manning Wardle. Both in good condition'. In *Colliery Guardian* of 12th October 1888 appeared this advertisement — 'Two locomotives for sale cheap — 9″ and 13″ cylinders. F. Cohen, New Basford, Nottingham'. The machinery register of C. D. Phillips, the locomotive dealer of Newport, Monmouthshire, dated January 1889 includes details of two locomotives that must surely be the same pair:

'15257.   Manning Wardle & Co. No. 40. four coupled. 9 x 14 cylinders. 2ft. wheels

15258.   Stephenson & Co, Newcastle on Tyne. No. 1959. 4 wheels coupled with bogie. Inside frames. Cylinders 13 x 18. wheels 3ft. 6in.'

Also given are many other technical details, but for our purpose the above will suffice; the register numbers suggest that Phillips was acting as an agent for the sale, but as they are consecutive, the locomotives could be from the same source. The Manning Wardle disappears after the end of 1889, presumably having been sold, but in the July 1890 register the 4-4-OT appears as No. 559g, indicating that it was then Phillips' property — and indeed she became *EMLYN No. 56* in his fleet. The alternative suggestion that the 4-4-OT bogie locomotive came from the North London Railway has been discounted by Mr. Higgins, who has consulted the NLR Minutes, in which there is nothing to support the idea.

The date of their arrival at Cogenhoe is not known. The extension of the line about 1869 to the quarries south south east of the village would seem a suitable time to introduce locomotives but it is doubtful if the Manning Wardle would have arrived by then, only having been built in 1861; it is more likely that the new management introduced them in 1880 or shortly afterwards.

The Cogenhoe concern was quite a big one for its day and in addition to ironstone quarrying a considerable amount of clay was dug, a brickworks being erected near the LNWR junction. Whellan (*History of Northamptonshire*, 1874, p.253) refers to 'the prosperous Cogenhoe iron ore industry'. The slump of the late 1880s proved too much however and on 16th July 1888 the whole equipment was put up for auction by Thos. Merry and included were the two locomotives, twenty tip wagons and two ten-ton standard gauge wagons. The track was lifted, the locomotives and rolling stock were sold, and the brickworks was razed to the ground. The quarries appear in MS until 1890 but we may presume this to be merely a paper continuation of the record in the absence of a correction.

There are still some traces of the Cogenhoe lines, suggesting that the original system was well laid, with earthworks where necessary. The course of the standard gauge line from the LNWR to the level crossing site can only faintly be discerned, and the junction area has mostly been incorporated into the field, while the site of the brickpit is denoted by a bulrush-filled pond; beyond the crossing the standard gauge course can be made out by the slight depression in the fields at various points, but is best seen when the ground is freshly ploughed, when it is picked out as an ochreous streak across the dark soil-remnants of ore fallen from wagons that rumbled across a century ago. The route of the narrow gauge line to The Firs starts as a well-preserved embankment at the road end, and finally as a cutting as higher ground is reached. In 'The Firs' (larches, in fact) the upper course of the tramway is marked by a hollow in the trees that runs to a wider gullet

Cogenhoe Quarries. Embankment that formerly carried the narrow gauge line to the quarry in 'The Firs' at the hill top. The contents of the tubs were emptied into standard gauge wagons on track that ran immediately behind the fence, then crossed the road to the left to reach the LNWR. View looking south from the road, 20th June 1979. (Eric Tonks)

trending northwest to southeast; this was probably widened later as an extension of the Whiston quarries, but an old face on the south side looks much older than World War I and almost certainly was as left by the Cogenhoe Iron Ore Co. West of this is a depression in higher ground, running south, and suggesting workings possibly for limestone; this section is completely overgrown. Of the mines there are no visible traces. At the western end of the system, a public footpath to Brafield leaves the road opposite the school and crosses an open grassy area of ground disturbed by the later quarrying activities and traversed by two well-defined cuttings whose directions converge on the tipping dock site; as the footpath descends to the stream bed, the former standard gauge line cutting can be seen, clearly defined to the terminus.

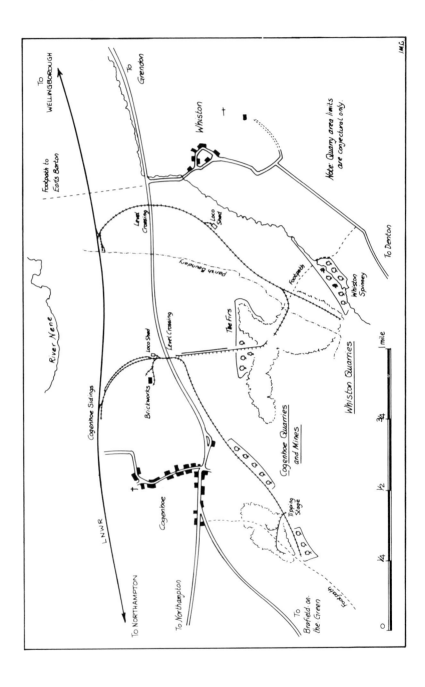

Grid References

836613	Junction with LNWR
838609	Level crossing
827601	Standard gauge terminus
839603	Narrow gauge terminus at The Firs
838609	Tipping dock from ng to sg (from The Firs)
828602	Tipping dock at Cogenhoe

Locomotives

Gauge; 4ft. 8½in.

-		0-4-0ST	OC	MW	40	1861	9 x 14in.	2ft. 0in.	(a) (1)
-		4-4-0ST	OC	RS	1959	1870	13 x 18in.	3ft. 6in.	(b) (1)

(a) ex W. H. & G. Dawes, Denby Ironworks, Derbyshire.
(b) ex South Leicester Colliery Co Ltd, Snibston Colliery.

(1) to C & D Phillips, dealers, Newport, Monmouthshire c 10/1888.

WHISTON QUARRIES

Owners: J. W. Pain; Whiston Ironstone Co from c.1915; Bloxham & Whiston Ironstone Co Ltd from 27th December 1917; Whiston Ironstone Co Ltd from 25th March 1919.

These quarries adjoined the more easterly of the Cogenhoe workings on a spur of high ground southwest of Whiston village, and had a short but chequered history, with four proprietors in a working life of less than ten years. They were opened in 1914 by the initiative of J. W. Pain after he had severed his connection with James Pain Ltd. J. W. Pain lived at Whiston Hall and presumably owned the freehold of the estate, as no details of the lease have been discovered; but there are fairly complete records of the equipment used.

The quarries were served by a standard gauge line laid from the LNWR, a distance of one mile; the line crossed the Castle Ashby road on the level and then ascended the hillside at a gradient of 1 in 20, turned south south west

Whiston Quarries. This picture of the No. 20 Ruston navvy is interesting in that few working views of this system have survived. c 1916. (Collection G. H. Starmer)

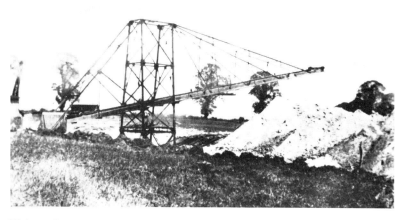

Whiston Quarries. The No. 5 transporter. The fate of this machine and of the navvy are unknown; but were new to Whiston and did less than five years' work, so there should have been plenty of life left to them. c 1916 (Collection G. H. Starmer)

Whiston Quarries. When the quarries closed, their solitary locomotive was transferred to Hunsbury Ironworks, where she was photographed on 14th March 1938.

(W. J. S. Meredith and NIRT)

at a somewhat easier gradient of about 1 in 30, finally disappearing into the woods surrounding the quarry area, where the rails were on the level. The quarries were some 40ft deep, and mechanical excavation was introduced in 1915 in the form of a 20-ton Ruston Proctor navvy, the following year working in conjunction with a No. 5 transporter; the ore was dug out manually and sold in the raw state. The overlying limestone was also quarried for fluxing purposes. Locally the workings were usually referred to as 'Pain's Whiston Pits' in allusion to their original proprietor, and the solitary locomotive bore the painted legend *J. W. PAIN, WHISTON MINES* at first. She was a standard 14in. Andrew Barclay supplied new in 1914; her original livery is unknown but was probably Barclay's standard green, lined black edged white, and she finished up at Finedon in a plain black livery with the name *WHISTON* in yellow letters on the saddle tank. It is possible that the name *WHISTON* was derived in the first place by leaving this word and painting out the others when Phipps took over. She was housed in a brick shed perched in an exposed position at the top of the steep incline, on ground built up on the hillside. The 'pot' was at the uphill end of the shed, indicating that the locomotive worked facing uphill, the obvious choice. A curious feature was that the shed had doors at both ends, the lintel of the uphill one having runners for a sliding door; the building therefore had a number of similarities with that at Bloxham quarries (those owned by Bloxham & Whiston Ironstone Co Ltd, **not** those of J. W. Pain) so much so that one suspects they were built by the same man, David Clifton of Bloxham. Possibly the locomotive stood in the open in Pain's time, or there may have been a simpler structure then, as there had been at Bloxham.

J. W. Pain had less success with his quarry enterprises than his father, and his term at Whiston was very brief, though clearly every effort had been made to work the site efficiently. Perhaps the proprietor was beset by troubles outside his quarrying activities. On 18th October 1917 the board of Bloxham Ironstone Co Ltd agreed, 'following informal discussion among the Directors, to purchase Whiston Ironstone Co from Mr. Wassell', their Chairman. The resulting agreement of 17th December 1917 records that Alfred Wassell, owner of the freehold property at Whiston, 'has spent large sums in securing the connection to the LNWR, opening an extensive working face of stone, purchase of wagons, digger, conveyor, locomotive and plant'. This would appear to be claiming credit for J. W. Pain's efforts, but evidently Wassell was associated with the enterprise from the start, possibly as manager; the LNWR siding diagram dated February 1915 is captioned 'Mr. Wassell's Siding' and refers to the 'Agreement dated 7.11.1914 with J. W. Pain Ironstone Mines'. The quarries were leased to Bloxham &

Whiston for 19 years from 29th September 1917, with an option for a further seven years, at a royalty of 4d per ton.

The new owners seem not to have had much success at Whiston, either. Twelve men were transferred to Bloxham in May 1918, and Whiston stone was offered to various ironmasters in the North Midlands and the Northeast, while T. H. Gray expressed interest in purchasing ganister, not iron ore. In August 1918 it was estimated that there were only 29 acres of stone visible — 'about three years' work' according to the board minutes, and calcining was considered in view of the decreased demand for raw stone. In November 1918 Pickering Phipps of Hunsbury Furnaces expressed interest in the Whiston quarries and in due course acquired them as from 25th March 1919, according to the minutes of the second general meeting of Bloxham & Whiston Ironstone Co Ltd. Production thereupon presumably went to Hunsbury Furnaces, the quarries being operated as Whiston Ironstone Co Ltd.

The only known description of Whiston in its working life appears in GSM; there was a north-south face 600 yards long, working westward across the spur of high ground, with the cover rising from 5ft. at the north end ('Firs Spinney') to 30ft. at the south end, the overburden being removed by the steam digger. All other operations were by hand and the ore was sold in the raw state. NSI adds that some ganister appears to have been worked.

The date when Whiston quarries ceased production is not clear. NSI states that the quarries were worked 'until about 1922', presumably taken from LQ, which lists Whiston in 1920 as an operating quarry and in 1922 as closed. On the other hand, Hunsbury Ironworks were closed in February 1920 and would not require ore after this date, so unless Whiston were supplying

Whiston Quarries. Once a familiar sight to travellers on road or rail, the locomotive shed perched on the hillside at the top of the steep but adhesion-worked incline. 25th April 1953.

(G. H. Starmer)

Whiston Quarries. Over the years the shed gradually succumbed to the invading elder bushes. Viewed from the trackbed on the north side, 20th June 1979.

(Eric Tonks)

elsewhere, the closure must have taken place about then. The locomotive went to Hunsbury for storage, in 1921 it is believed, and was used in the demolition of the plant before being transferred to Finedon quarries by the new owners, Richard Thomas & Co Ltd. During the postwar years so many ironstone quarries went out of production that individual closures sometimes escaped record, Whiston among them; and in this unsatisfactory state we leave the question until someone can perhaps come forward with a definite date. The LNWR sidings were removed 12th August 1923.

The track was lifted, but the brick locomotive shed survived the closure as a shelter for farm implements, and was a familiar sight to travellers on the road and railway. The building had little or no maintenance and by 1974 had been reduced to the west wall; in 1977 there was a heap of brickwork and wood, and one chimney (of the sand-drier?) was still standing. The route of the line used to be easy to pick out; between railway and road the trackbed was on ground level (river level, almost) and on a Spring visit in May 1967 Pete Staughton noted that from the vicinity of the loco. shed the course of the line on this section could be seen as 'an orange-brown streak across the fields', while at harvest time the corn was yellower. Two field gates were on the site of the original level crossing, but that on the south side was removed when a nurseryman occupied part of the field here for a few years. On the south side of the road, the course of the line was clear all the way to the quarries, and beyond the locomotive shed ruins there are excellent views across the valley. This applied up to 1979 and possibly later, but by 1985 most of this route had been ploughed out, with just a gap in the hedge where the line passed through. The principal working seems to have been a face running south south west (agreeing with the description in GSM), and the final gullet remains, now heavily overgrown with ash trees on the outer (east) side and larches on the hill-and-dale. A short way along this gullet from the point where the tramway enters the trees, a public footpath from Castle Ashby to Cogenhoe crosses the site and trails along another gullet running northwest. Whether this was ever part of the Whiston system is not clear; probably it was to some extent, but an old face at the western end probably dates from Cogenhoe Iron Ore Co days.

Grid References

845613	Junction with LNWR
847609	Level Crossing
846606	Locomotive shed
842602	Top of incline
841601	Junction to quarry
840598	Terminus of line to south

Locomotive

Gauge; 4ft. 8½in.

WHISTON		0-4-0ST	OC	AB	1333	1914	14 x 22in.	3ft. 3in.	New 9/1914 (1)

(1) to Hunsbury Hill Ironworks, 1921.

Quarry Machines

No. 20	S. Navvy	RP	436	1915	2¾ Cu.Yds.	31ft.	New 8/1915	s/s
No. 5	Transporter	RP	471	1916			New 10/1916	s/s

EARLS BARTON QUARRIES

Owners: Earls Barton Iron Ore Co Ltd

This was another wartime affair as far as production was concerned, though the company had been formed in 1913 (after promising results from trial holes sunk in August 1911) under the joint ownership of Stanton Ironworks Co Ltd, Shelton Iron, Steel & Coal Co Ltd, Newton Chambers & Co Ltd, and Midland Coal, Coke & Iron Co Ltd — a formidable mouthful for so small a concern; with it we come to an example of an aerial ropeway. This was erected in 1913/4 to convey the ore to Castle Ashby & Earls Barton station on the LNWR Northampton-Peterborough line, south of the Nene, the propensity of which to periodic heavy flooding would have made a tramway from the north of the river impracticable, though the quarries were no more elevated than those at Whiston.

The leases of ground and wayleaves required for this system have been preserved in Northamptonshire Record Office, and as they provide an interesting insight into the complexities involved in opening even a small quarry, we quote the particulars in some detail. The principal quarrying area lay to the immediate north and east of Earls Barton, on land leased from William Chetwode Whitworth, for thirty years commencing 29th September 1913, and comprising 'several closes of freehold pasture and arable land' — fourteen in fact — to a total of just over 193 acres along the crest of the ridge about the 320ft. level. A surface annual rent of £5 per acre was set and a royalty of 5d per ton for ironstone carried (or ½d per ton for materials from other estates) with a minimum annual payment of £300. It was permitted to lay tramways 'within the limits of deviation to be hereafter agreed' — which would presumably allow the slewing customary in quarrying — but in Field 247 the tramway was to be confined to the strip immediately adjacent to the Wellingborough road, i.e. the western side of the field; this was doubtless to ensure that the tramway did not encroach upon the grounds of New Barton Grange. No calcining was to be permitted — again possibly because this could impair the view from the Grange windows!

The other principal lease was granted by John Clark and John Richardson, for thirty years commencing 25th March 1913, for the 'Mining of Iron Ore and Wayleaves at Earls Barton'. The total area of nearly 179 acres included four fields north of the Doddington road just on the 300ft. contour and within the ironstone field, but the remaining area was that occupied by tramway and ropeway; a surface rent of £5 per acre was levied for the ground used for sidings, but £4 per acre on that used for workings or tramways (?including the ropeway) plus a royalty of 4d per ton of ironstone carried on it, with a minimum of £50 per year. A further proviso was that carrier buckets on the ropeway were not to be less than 10ft. from the ground.

Other wayleaves and leases were made with:-

Henry Minshull Stockdale of Mears Ashby Hall for 30 years commencing 25th March 1913 for a field each side of the LNWR; a sum of £10 per acre was charged for land under the ropeway or 'injuriously affected by machinery', and a wayleave rent of ten guineas for ironstone.

The Ecclesiastical Commissioners for 1½ acres of meadow land adjacent to the LNWR station and which was in the glebe attached to Castle Ashby Parish Church. This was for 40 years from 24th July 1913 at £10 per year.

Wellingborough Rural District Council from 3rd September 1913 for making subways under the roads from Earls Barton to Wellingborough and Doddington, to enable the company to lay a tramway for conveying ironstone. £2 annual rent was payable. The bridges could be of brick or of iron girders and concrete. Provision was made for the company to determine (i.e. bring to an end) the arrangement at any time, but after 1st January 1921 either side could do so subject to six months notice. On completion of ironstone working, the company must 'fill in the bridges in a solid manner' if requested by the council so to do. The company sought originally to cross the roads on the level, but Earls Barton Parish Council, while they wished to encourage the company for the good of the village, thought level crossings would be dangerous (as reported in the *Kettering Leader*, 4th July 1913).

Finally, there was a lease with Lady Wantage for land at Mears Ashby, dated 1st April 1916 for 30 years. £5 per acre was payable when the land was in use or until returned to a state fit for agricultural use, and royalties of 4d per ton for ironstone and 3d per ton for limestone and sand quarried. £20 was the minimum payment for the first year, £25 for the second and third years and £100 for the fourth year. The precise location of this area is not given but it was probably on the north side of the main Northampton-Wellingborough road (where there is a stretch of ironstone-bearing land towards Mears Ashby) and if so was not opened up; the lease is not included in those 'determined' at the closure, which again suggests it was never actively taken up.

The engineers working for the company that built the ropeway lodged at the home of the Knight family, whose young son Frank was an enthralled spectator of the Earls Barton system under construction and in production; and in late 1985 he recounted the events that had made such a lasting impression on his mind, then at its most receptive, lending colour to the

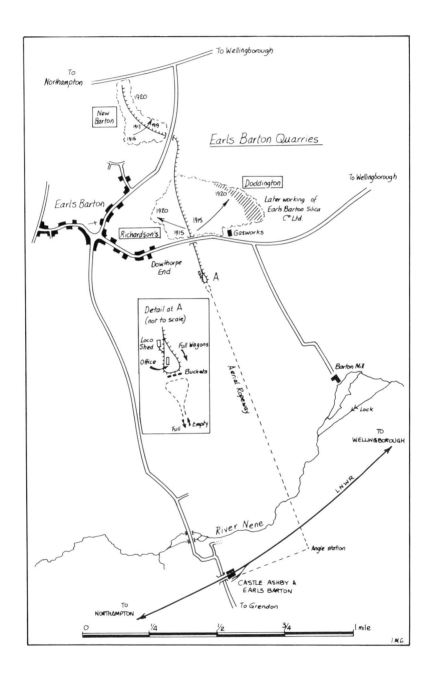

data from the archives.

The quarrying area was on the north side of Doddington Road and a 3ft. gauge tramway was constructed between this and the ropeway terminal, which was about 200 yards south of the road, at Dowthorpe End. At this point the tramway was in the form of a loop, carried on a mound built up on the hillside, and along the southern edge of the mound was a series of bins into which the side-tipping wagons emptied their loads; the ropeway buckets were filled from these bins. The tramway was on a slight gradient towards the southern end, the locomotive pushing up the eastern arm of the loop a train of wagons, which were then manhandled along the line of bins and run off by gravity on the other side for collection by the locomotive. The loco. shed was on the western arm of the loop, with the office close by.

The ropeway was supplied by Bullivant's Aerial Ropeways Ltd, of Millwall, London, and was carried on 17 trestles, with a bridge over the railway and an angle station south of this, the distance between loading and angle stations being just one mile; from the latter point the cable was carried east a further quarter mile to the discharging point in the station goods yard, where the buckets were emptied by a simple mechanism and returned upside down (to avoid filling with water in wet weather) and were righted when detached from the cable at the loading station. Shunting of railway wagons at the station was performed by a horse. The cable was 1½in. in diameter and at the 'tip' ran round a wheel 4ft. in diameter, then below the loading bins to a tensioning weight that was adjusted according to the loading of the cable, then up to another 4ft. wheel to receive the empty buckets. Power was provided by a 35 horsepower 'National' gas engine housed at the 'tip'; since the loaded buckets were moving downhill, gravity did most of the work and the gas engine served to keep things running smoothly. At the 'tip' the ropeway buckets were detached from the cable and pushed by hand beneath the bins for filling and were automatically reclipped to the cable on leaving the bins.

The main line of the tramway ran north north east for about half a mile, passing beneath Doddington Road by a bridge, with a passing loop just to the north of this, then running close to Wellingborough Road, as it was required by the lease to do. This section was mainly on a rising gradient northwards. The bridge under Doddington Road collapsed when half completed, fortunately without anyone being injured. During the early construction period horses were used for haulage but in 1914 a locomotive was obtained new from Hudswell Clarke; she was an 0-4-2ST, a type unusual but not unknown in the ironstone industry; she carried the name *NANNIE* in black paint on the saddle and was painted dark red. She appears

143

Earls Barton Quarries. Only one locomotive was used, a 0-4-2ST named *NANNIE*, and shown here with 'gaffer' and workmen. Date c 1919. When *NANNIE* was away for overhaul in 1920 she was replaced by Manning Wardle 0-4-0ST.

(Collection J. E. & M. L. Palmer)

to have been worked hard, as could be expected in wartime and was maintained in fine condition by the blacksmith, who worked nights at the shed. She went away to be rebuilt by the makers in 1920, during which period she was replaced by a standard Manning Wardle 0-4-0ST from Orton quarries.

Wagons were side-tippers, and at closure there were 76—52 'old type' (wood) and 24 'new type' (steel); it is known that W. G. Bagnall Ltd supplied 12 wagons in 1919, of steel and with a capacity of 40 cubic feet, so probably all 24 were of this type. Coal for the locomotives and quarry machines was carried in a wagon with an underframe on bogies, as found on several other narrow gauge systems, e.g. Loddington.

There were three quarries, the first to be opened being Richardson's pit immediately north of the Doddington road; working from the outcrop was on both sides of the tramway, the first strips being in the west side. According to Stanton Ironworks records (kindly extracted by Alister Gilks, MIPR, Press and Information Officer, Stanton & Staveley) production commenced 1st July 1915. Very shortly afterwards, the New Barton pit was developed, reached by a bridge under Wellingborough Road, and here were two fields worked in a clockwise direction and under a few feet of sandy cover. New Barton was a Victorian extension on the north side of the old village, which boasts a fine Saxon church. Last to be opened up was the longer Doddington pit to the east, where the overburden went up to 18ft. Richardson's pit seems to have been worked 1915-17, then in 1920, New

Barton 1915-17 and then from late 1919, hence Doddington was probably worked 1918/9. The stone at the Doddington pit proved to be rather siliceous and the overburden included a thick layer of white silica sand and silt. It seems likely that the poor quality of the ironstone, and the interference from the sand, led to the abandonment of the pit and the reopening of the New Barton and Richardson's pits. The output was sent to the ironworks of the partners, and management of the site seems to have been exercised by Stanton.

In the earlier years, and probably always in Richardson's pit, the familiar 'plank and barrow' method of hand operation was employed; the locomotive placed wagons at intervals along the working face, one for each loader, and collected them when full. Shortly after the end of the war, quarrying equipment on quite a generous scale for a small system was supplied by Ruston Proctor—a 20-ton long-jib navvy, new in 1918; and an 18-ton short-jib navvy and a No. 5 transporter, new in 1919. The two latter machines worked in conjunction in the deeper Doddington Pit along with another digger—either the long-jib navvy or a 20 ton navvy acquired secondhand, the other machine working at New Barton pit. In addition to trouble with silica, flooding occurred in the Doddington pit, and after one very wet weekend, when the track and wagons were all under water a culvert was driven to take the excess down the hillside to the Nene.

Closure of the quarries is recorded by Hewlett as due to the variable character of the stone and trouble with overlying sand; and while these factors undoubtedly played their part, the postwar drop in demand had its effect also. Stanton furnaces were damped down in 1921 and the company's ironstone quarries were obliged to cease operations on 24th March 1921, the date quoted by Mr. Gilks; Earls Barton did not reopen, probably because of the factors just mentioned. Yet the fact that the Hudswell Clarke locomotive was rebuilt in 1920 suggests that it had been worked intensively during the war years and that it was expected to give many more years service at the quarries. The last date on the plans attached to the leases is September 1920, and as the plans seem to have been marked up annually, closure may be assumed to have taken place before September 1921, and most likely on March 24th 1921. The quarries then lay dormant for two years, after which time the closure must have been accepted as permanent, and steps were taken to dismantle the system and dispose of the equipment. An inventory appears on twelve foolscap sheets deposited in the Northamptonshire Record Office, along with correspondence relating to the closure; so that the death of this little system is almost as well recorded as its birth. Its life, unfortunately, is passed by in silence, apart from what may be inferred from the details given in the files, and what we have learnt from Frank Knight.

The first letter in the correspondence on closure is dated 24th October 1923, and arrangements were immediately put in hand to terminate the leases from W. C. Whitworth, Clark and Richardson, and H. M. Stockdale, all on 25th March 1924. Additional leases are mentioned, too, from F. L. J. Matthews for seven years from 29th September 1917, and from a Mr. Hornby, again to terminate 25th March 1924; and from a Mr. S. A. Middleton for three years from 25th November 1919, to be terminated 25th December 1923. The location of these parcels of land has not been discovered—possibly they were fields near the Doddington road, or in the village.

The most interesting document is the inventory made in December 1923, which includes minutiae of equipment more interesting sociologically than industrially; but the list has provided a wealth of detail on the tramway and quarry plant in general. Unfortunately, the disposal of these things is not recorded, though we know the fate of some of them from other sources; these disposals evidently took place in 1924. The track was lifted and the ground restored according to the provisions of the leases. The Clark & Richardson lease required the land to be levelled, the surface soil replaced and fences cut through to be replaced by 'double quicks' (a double line of hawthorn hedge). The Whitworth lease also required levelling and resoiling (or returfing in the case of pasture) or the payment of £50 per acre in lieu if the ground were too difficult for simple restoration. A further provision was that plant and machinery were to be offered to the lessor at a fair price 'as a going concern'. The Ecclesiastical Commissioners asked for their land to be restored to cultivation or the payment of £60 per acre for liquidated damages.

Finally, the Wellingborough RDC demanded the filling in of the bridges (as they were entitled to do) and the quarry company complied, grumbling nonetheless to the clerk of the council in a letter dated 24th November 1924:- '...will fill bridges solidly and lay pipe through same to carry away water from upper to lower levels... The County Council has not required ironstone companies to destroy arches in the way your council have required the Earls Barton Iron Ore Co to do, but have been satisfied to leave the arches standing as built' Concrete filling was used (see *Kettering Leader* 1st February 1924). The company was struck off the register in April 1927.

Thus the simple remains passed into oblivion. However, we have already alluded to the thick bed of white silica sand that overlay the ironstone and interfered with quarrying; this sand is in considerable demand for furnace lining, and the bed of it in the Doddington pit was opened up by the Earls

Barton Silica Co Ltd, probably about 1925. The output was conveyed over a 2ft. gauge line operated by diesel locomotives to a point close to the junction to the New Barton pit and loaded into lorries for despatch. The sand (or 'ganister' as it is more familiarly known) occurs in close proximity to ironstone in several quarries in Northamptonshire, sometimes being worked alongside it (as at Pitsford, Cranford and Islip) sometimes subsequent to it (as at Earls Barton and Burton Latimer). The Earls Barton 2ft. line is interesting in being the final working location of the pioneer Ruston & Hornsby diesel locomotive, No. 163997, which bore an unusual curved nameplate, *FURY.*

There has been much building of houses at Earls Barton, particularly since World War II, and this has covered much of the site of the New Barton quarries; but the parapet of the bridge on the east side of Wellingborough Road remains, of red brick surmounted by a concrete coping of triangular section, and the side pillars topped with a pyramidal concrete casting. The ground beneath has been filled in as specified, and the parapet appears to be a length of wall in the line of the hedge. The piece of ground between the road and New Barton Grange is as open as in the days of the original lease, and the course of the tramway can be observed as a depression in the field.

Earls Barton Quarries. The quarry site was later taken over by Earls Barton Silica Co Ltd, working the upper layers for ganister. Our picture of May 1949 shows the 2ft. gauge tramway and a 10RB diesel shovel in the former Doddington pit.   (BGS)

Earls Barton Quarries. Bridge parapet on Wellingborough Road, New Barton. The pit by the same name was across the road. 9th May 1984. (Eric Tonks)

The site of the former tramway junction bears little evidence of it but, until the late 1970s, plenty of the activities of the silica company, including a tipping dock with the locomotive shed underneath, complete with pit and pieces of track could be seen; there was also a long gullet with, in 1977, a very rusty 10RB diesel digger. In 1979 houses were being erected on land reclaimed from the west end of the gullet, but the rest has been left intact and unrestored, and runs for about a quarter of a mile, littered with lengths of rail and bits of old 2ft. gauge wagons. The thick layer of white silica sand is very clearly defined, with darker sand in the overburden. The Doddington ironstone quarry is recorded in GSM as having been worked northeast from the Doddington road, and the present quarry is an extension of it northerly, and outside the original ironstone lease. Worked-out ground starts from a belt of trees growing on mounds of soil, to the south of the present quarry.

South of the junction to New Barton and Doddington pits, building in the early 1980s has obscured the depressions in the ground that marked the site of Richardson's pit, and the course of the tramway (until then just discernible as a depression partly filled with undergrowth) at the end forming the garden of a house on the north side of Doddington Road; on the south side of the road the bridge parapet is in the hedge of No. 66, and is similar to the Wellingborough Road example. For some distance south the ground is covered by new houses, but the hump on the hillside overlooking the Nene valley, where the 'tip' was situated, still stands as a very solid reminder of past industry at the end of the cul-de-sac named 'Milbury', which was the name of the field on the same site; of ironstone rubble and with a fair number of trees atop, and known as 'The Knoll' it looks quite an imposing earthwork, but we wonder how many of the new residents are aware of its origin! A block of concrete on the bank marks the start of the range of bins. The locomotive shed survived until the building of the houses in Colden Close. In the fields below, the base of one of the pylons survives in the form of four blocks of stone, each about a yard square, arranged in a diamond pattern. At the station site, the concrete foundations of the yard are visible.

Grid References

857643	Bridge under Wellingborough Road
858637	Bridge under Doddington Road
857640	Locomotive shed
859635	Ropeway loading point
860631	Pylon base

Locomotives

Gauge; 3ft. 0in.

NANNIE	0-4-2ST	OC	HC	1087	1914	9½ x 15in.	2ft. 6½in.	New 9/1914	(1)
LIZZIE	0-4-0ST	OC	MW	1038	1887	9½ x 14in.	2ft. 9in.	(a)	(2)

(a) ex Orton Quarries, near Loddington c 1920.

(1) to Bloxham & Whiston Ironstone Co Ltd, Harringworth Quarries 1924.
(2) to Stanton Ironworks Co Ltd, Rothwell Hill Quarries c 1921.

Quarry Machines

No. 20	S. Navvy. Long Jib	RH	528	1918			New 10/1918	(1)
No. 18	S. Navvy	RH	562	1919			New 9/1919	(2)
No. 5	SND Transporter	RH	567	1919			New 12/1919	(2)
No. 18	S. Navvy	RH	509	1918	2¾ Cu.Yds.	31ft.	(a)	(3)

(a) ex Furness Shipbuilding Co Ltd.

(1) to Buckminster Quarries c 1921.
(2) to Islip Iron Co Ltd c 1924.
(3) to Cargo Fleet Iron Co Ltd, Twywell Quarries.

Earls Barton Quarries. No photographs of the aerial ropeway from the hilltop to the LNWR seem to have survived, but the 'tip', the artificial mound built up to accommodate the loading station, remains among all the new housing. 9th May 1984. Eric Tonks)

Earls Barton Quarries. The base of one of the pylons in the field below the village (on the horizon). 9th May 1984. (Eric Tonks)

NORTHERN GROUP

The LNWR Market Harborough line runs from Northampton northwards up the Maidwell valley, formed by a tributary of the Nene. A belt of ironstone under thin cover lay to the east of this and was exploited at Brixworth from 1863 up to the end of World War II: there was a small working at Lamport in the 1880s, whilst World War I saw the introduction of quarrying at Scaldwell and Hanging Houghton, followed by Pitsford shortly afterwards. Interest from the transport angle lies in the narrow gauge tramways, at Brixworth operating almost unchanged for nearly 70 years, and at Scaldwell and Hanging Houghton working in conjunction with an aerial ropeway. The Stanton company's Orton quarries, connecting to the LNWR further north, belong geographically to the Kettering area, under which they are described.

DALLINGTON QUARRY

Owners: Dallington Iron Ore Co Ltd

The scattered references to workings at Dallington are few, but even so it is difficult to reconcile them into one coherent picture. MS records this location for 1859 only, as Dallington Iron Ore Co Ltd. In his *Geology of parts of Northamptonshire and Warwickshire* (Memoirs of the Geological Survey, 1861), W. T. Aveline states that 'near Dallington Mill, on the east side of the Northampton and Market Harborough Railway, the sand is worked for ironstone'; properly speaking, this is not Dallington Mill, but Kingsthorpe Upper Mill, now demolished. In the Duke of Grafton papers in Northamptonshire Record Office are letters between D. Wheldon, of the Dallington Iron Ore Works, and John Simpson, the Duke's agent, following a meeting on 15th June 1860, when Wheldon had apparently raised the question of leasing some ground from the Duke; nothing came of this, but the 1883 *Handbook of Stations* lists 'Wheldon's Siding' between Northampton and Pitsford stations. The implication therefore is that the site quoted by Aveline was that used by Wheldon, who presumably had had authority to do some preliminary work in 1859. The site lies about three quarters of a mile south of Boughton Crossing, on the south side of a public footpath; in 1981 the rough field suggested possible early quarrying activities. The site was very small, and is seems doubtful if a tramway was laid, though the LNWR was conveniently close, so the possibility cannot be ruled out. In 1984-6 the area was built upon.

Grid References

739641   Quarry site

DALLINGTON QUARRIES

Owners: G. E. Bevan & Co Ltd

While this company's activities at Dallington are not recorded in MS, it appears from contemporary newspaper reports (for which we are indebted to Geoffrey Starmer) that they were on a considerably bigger scale than Wheldon's described above. At first we assumed they were at the same site, but it seems more likely that this was not the case.

In 1859 G. E. Bevan & Co Ltd were reported to be 'contemplating a very large business at Dallington' and appear to have operated here up to 1863, when they had nearly exhausted the supply of ore here, and were opening 'mines' at Blisworth and Wellingborough. That they used a horse-worked tramway is confirmed by a report in the *Northampton Mercury* of 16th June 1860 of an accident to an employee who was 'attending the horses drawing the trucks at the ironstone pit' and was run over by a truck.

The location of the quarries is unknown, but it does not sound like the Wheldon site, and an alternative was suggested by a map of 1864, revised to 31st December 1872, discovered by Geoffrey Webb in BTC archives; this shows the Northampton-Market Harborough branch, with a siding on the west side 33 chains north of Northampton Castle station—this siding noted as serving a quarry and as removed by 1872. The site would be fairly close to Duston, where Bevans are known to have worked from 1863 and possibly earlier. The Grafton papers contain correspondence in 1860 and onwards between the Duke's agent and William Brown, who had some associations with G. E. Bevan & Co, concerning Dallington, but is not explicit as to the site. That is all we know at present, with as many guesses as facts; if the site is as we have supposed, there is no hope of seeing anything on the ground, which has long been built over by houses or railway sidings. As for the tramway, again we don't know, but it was probably standard gauge, as at Duston.

Grid Reference

745615 approx.   Believed site of quarry.

PITSFORD QUARRIES

Owners: Pitsford Ironstone Co: Staveley Minerals Ltd from 7th March 1961: Byfield Ironstone Co Ltd from September 1962.

Two miles north of the transient Dallington quarries we reach the Pitsford quarries, which were the last of those connected with the Northampton-Market Harborough line to be opened. The nominal owners were Pitsford Ironstone Co, a company owned jointly by Staveley Coal & Iron Co Ltd, Park Gate Iron & Steel Co Ltd and Bestwood Coal & Iron Co Ltd, with Staveley exercising controlling interest. Negotiations with Colonel Howard Vyse for the leasing of land for ironstone extraction began about the end of World War I and when the opportunity came in 1920 to extend the leased area, expected to yield $4\frac{1}{4}$ million tons of ore, it was decided to form the ironstone company. The indenture with 'Staveley Coal & Iron Co Ltd and others' was dated 31st December 1920 but the lease was 'back-dated' to 29th September 1919 for the term of 50 years and a royalty of 5d per ton; the area was bounded by the LNWR for about a third of a mile but eastwards extended further north and south from Brampton Lane to the White Hills

Pitsford Quarries. The exchange sidings on the Northampton-Market Harborough line, looking north, 1st July 1953. The line to the quarry can be seen immediately in front of the smokebox of the 'Class 4'. (G. H. Starmer)

Pitsford Quarries. The yard close to the BR line (in the valley beyond). At right centre is the locomotive shed with water tank in front and the old No. 2 behind. At left centre is the building that once housed *PIXIE*. Note the 2ft. wagon bodies nearby. 19th September 1959.　　　　　　　　　　　　　　　　　　　　(S. A. Leleux)

district of Broughton, with the A508 as the eastern boundary for most of the way.

The siding agreement with the LNWR was dated 29th November 1921. Operations on the site commenced in 1923 and the first record of production was in 1925; this period was one of slack demand, so the proprietors possibly did not hurry things. The quarries were on a spur of ground around the 300ft. contour, only slightly elevated above the LMS line at about 240ft., and a standard gauge line was laid from a north-facing junction south of Pitsford & Brampton station, in a curve and at a fairly stiff gradient to the first workings of almost outcropping stone south east of Brampton Lane. The locomotive shed of corrugated iron and office of wood were near the junction and there was no access other than along railway tracks, the nearest vehicle approach being the private road to a farm; for a system installed during the Motor Age this was perhaps a little surprising, but it obtained also at Lamport.

Five small parcels of land, totalling about 40 acres, near to and on both sides of the main road at Pitsford, were leased from J. H. Marlow for 31 years from 29th September 1938, i.e. to terminate at the same time as the principal lease. This was followed by the purchase on 7th October 1941 of a large area of freehold land — 917 acres (563 acres in Pitsford parish, 245 in Broughton

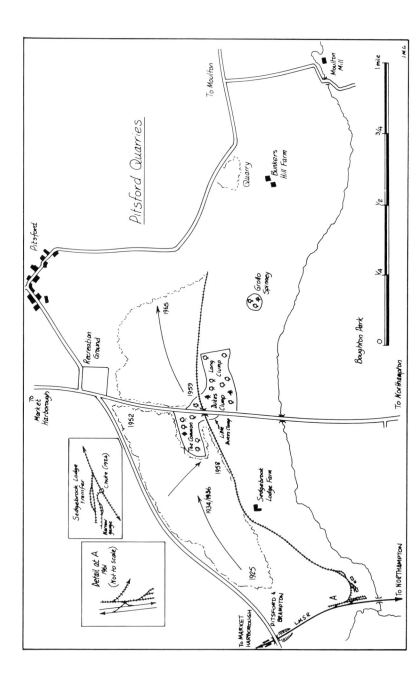

parish and 109 in Moulton parish). This was all on the higher ground in the vicinity of Pitsford village, almost surrounding the latter, and stretched north of Brampton Lane to the stream and south of Pitsford in a broad band almost as far as Moulton village.

The use of quarry machinery had been decided upon from the outset, and a No. 135 steam stripping shovel came new from Ruston & Hornsby in 1925; she had a marine boiler, a jib length of 75ft. with a dumping radius of 85ft., and weighed about 160 tons. Apart from her, the known quarry machines were of standard designs common to the ironstone fields; a 15-ton steam navvy was obtained in 1933 but, before that, loading was by hand. A small 21RB diesel shovel supplied in 1936 may have been for use on the calcine bank.

Pitsford Quarries. Working in the quarry as it approached the main road appears to have been somewhat confined. Shown here is the No. 135 stripping shovel with jib lowered, and a small diesel loading shovel at the face; *PITSFORD* has just brought up a set of empties. On the top of the quarry is a rock drill. 5th March 1954. (G. H. Starmer)

Pitsford Quarries.
No. 4 Ruston diesel digger handling ganister. c 1935.
(G. Rowley)

An unusual attraction for the railway enthusiast was the introduction of a 2ft. gauge system; this was operated by a standard Bagnall locomotive, *PIXIE*, well known since her acquisition by the late Rev. E. R. Boston at Cadeby Rectory. She came from Pilton quarries when Pitsford was first opened and returned there some five years later, but came back to Pitsford in 1932. The main purpose of this line was the removal of ganister (silica) from the overlying beds, but initially *PIXIE* may also have been employed in opening up the quarry lines as she had done at Pilton. The layout of the narrow gauge line in its earlier period is shown on the OS with a 'chute' at the point where the narrow gauge was carried over the standard gauge. Doubtless a similar layout obtained in the later period, but further up the hillside. 'Ganistering' ceased about 1939, when *PIXIE* was relegated to a tiny wooden shed by the office, without track, and surrounded by rubbish of all kinds. However, she was eventually taken to Cranford for another spell of ganistering. Wagons were steel V-section side-tippers. *PIXIE's* livery at Pitsford was green lined white (outer) and red (inner) with red frames and red-backed nameplates.

The surveyor's plans at Brigstock Manor showed a very simple series of annual 'cuts' of ironstone; with the passage of time the main tramway was extended as the quarrying area moved eastwards, and from the middle 1930s the working face was reached from a reversing point by Sedgebrook Lodge Farm; but the latter system was eventually replaced by a through line, though retaining a loop. Originally the owners' own wagons were probably used, but later calcining was introduced, involving the use of wooden side-tipping wagons with bodies 6ft. 6in. x 10ft. x 3ft. 3in.; the ore was despatched in ordinary railway wagons, which were used throughout when calcining was discontinued. Probably the calcining operations were conducted in the area of the reversing point. With the simplified layout it was only necessary for one locomotive in steam to push the empty wagons to the working face, collect full ones left in a loop and return to the BR sidings. By 1950 the main tramway was one mile long and the quarry face was nearing the corner of Brampton Lane (also called Station Road) and the Northampton-Market Harborough road (A508), and the depth of overburden to be removed increased as the working face moved north and east.

Permission to take the rail line under the A508 to open up the area to the east was granted by Northamptonshire County Council on 30th July 1954, and the road had to be temporarily diverted to the west while the concrete-lined tunnel was being constructed. The new quarry was opened for production about March 1959. Track in the quarry itself, unlike the flat-bottomed rail on the main tramway, was laid in secondhand chairs stamped 'S.R.1933' etc. At this time the intermediate siding by the farm was removed.

One casualty of the move was the large steam navvy, for many years a familiar sight working away in the quarry on the west side of the A508; it was considered too expensive to move it to the new site, and a new Ruston Bucyrus 5W electric walking dragline and a Ransomes & Rapier 490 electric shovel were obtained. In the course of time the working face moved eastwards fanwise away from the road, the intervening ground being returned to cultivation; but the playing field at the corner of the road to Pitsford village was left intact. As will be seen from the map, entry to the quarry necessitated a reversal, but the procedure was not always the same. At first (1959/60) the locomotive pushed the empties to the top, ran round them at the terminal loop and pushed them to the quarry; the full wagons were then removed by the same process in reverse. By 1963 this had been modified; the locomotive pushed the empties from the loop by the shed up to the terminal loop, then uncoupled and ran round and forward light engine to the quarry, where it ran round the full wagons and propelled them to the loop alongside the empties, which it then pulled to the quarry. As there was a stiff bank to the pit, this usually made a fine pyrotechnic display! The locomotive then returned to the full wagons and hauled them to the BR end of the line.

The locomotive history is fairly simple but the stock was not lacking in variety. *PITSFORD*, one of the handsome Avonsides favoured by the Staveley group, came new here and worked the line apparently unaided until the middle 1930s; she came in a livery of Brunswick green lined black edged with white, with green wheels and red-backed brass nameplates,

Pitsford Quarries. *PITSFORD* one of the handsome Avonside 0-6-0ST with 15in. cylinders, that Staveley used in many of their quarries. 26th July 1949.

(Ken Cooper/IRS Collection)

and had a fine copper-capped chimney. In 1957 she was repainted at Pitsford in a more elaborate livery—common to Staveley quarries at the time—of green lined black edged red on the outside and yellow on the inside, with an intricate corner pattern; and red connecting rods. This painting was presumably carried out by a crew who travelled from one quarry to another in the group, applying similar liveries; but in this case they must have been in a bit of a hurry, as the yellow edging was omitted on the right-hand side!

No. 2 was undoubtedly the most interesting locomotive at Pitsford by reason of its age, and in the middle 1950s was the oldest Manning Wardle known to be in use in this country. She came in the mid-thirties from Charwelton and was in the Park Gate brown livery, with *No. 2* painted in white on the tank; an underlying *No. 3* could also be discerned thereon, so probably there had been some swapping of tanks at some time. She acted as a spare to *PITSFORD* when the latter was under repair, but her four-coupled wheels and 12in. cylinders made her a poor substitute in taking empties up the bank and even more so when holding them on the downhill trip, with the fireman hanging on to the brake. There was not much

Pitsford Quarries. Vintage Manning Wardle locomotive approaches the BR junction, 1st July 1953. (G. H. Starmer)

protection for the crew, either! Whilst there is no positive information on the point, it is possible that she was acquired initially to operate the calcine bank; when calcining was practised, a further locomotive would be necessary, and the little Manning Wardle would be quite capable of this lighter work. She was dumped out of use in 1959 and lost her chimney, but in October the boiler was passed for further use — which, however, never came off, as by then the Hudswell Clarke had arrived. *No. 2* was cut up in January 1964, and a number of 'Ship Canal' wooden side-tipping wagons that were stored alongside her were burnt up at the same time. The 0-6-0ST *IRENE* came to Pilton quarries in Rutland from Midland Ironstone Co Ltd, Frodingham and was re-loaned to Pitsford; this confirmation of stories of *IRENE* working at Pitsford comes from an inventory of Staveley and Park Gate quarry locomotives dated October 1932, and preserved by Bert Smith of Cranford. In March 1966 a nameplate *IRENE* was discovered in the stores, and some of the men referred to *No. 2* as *IRENE*, so it may possibly have been intended to give her the name sometime. *PITSFORD* was loaned to Midland Ironstone in 1934, where there was a break in production at Pitsford — presumably closure for perhaps a year.

Pitsford Quarries. The last locomotive was a Hudswell Clarke that came in 1957 from Appleby-Frodingham steelworks. She was painted in a livery of light green lined black edged with yellow, and is seen here coming up the bank from the BR sidings, 9th May 1960. (Ivo Peters)

The last arrival was a Hudswell Clarke, one of the many steam locomotives displaced by diesels at Appleby-Frodingham steelworks; she was given a livery of light green, lined black edged yellow on the inside, and the solid numbers *65* on the cabsides, painted red on the front and black on the sides; and red coupling rods. She was a little more powerful than *PITSFORD* and therefore good at tackling the bank, but when the quarry face was beyond the main road *65* had barely sufficient water capacity for the round trip. Nevertheless the two locomotives were used in turn, even when the quarry was quite close to Pitsford village.

In 1963 the quarries were described as busy, but the middle-sixties slump in the iron ore industry brought rumours of closure in the spring of 1965, when production was down to 2,000 tons per week, sent to Staveley and Renishaw ironworks, and it was to the latter that the last load was despatched on 27th August 1965. Dismantling of the rail system commenced shortly afterwards, *PITSFORD* being used for the work, hauling rails by means of chains attached to the front bufferbeam; lifting continued through the winter and by the end of February 1966 all track had gone down to the curve by the shed. The *Northampton Chronicle & Echo* carried an account of the line in its issue of 18th February 1966. Some narrow gauge relics that had lain untouched for years were disposed of for scrap at this time (February) — four jubilee wagon bodies and some underframes with screw brake, half buried in brambles by *PIXIE's* shed, and some lengths of rail. In the fitting shop there were also some large wooden sieves used for 'sorting the stone' in early days in conjunction with jubilee wagons; it is not clear whether ironstone or ganister is referred to in this connection. The last few lengths of standard gauge rail were lifted by a 10RB crane in May and early June 1966, the machine having completed the filling of the quarry and redistributing the topsoil piled on one side in the standard manner. The former cutting was filled to field level east of the main road, but the route on the west was not restored — indeed the sleepers were still on the site.

By this time both the remaining locomotives had been sold to the preservation movement. As stated earlier, the only access for road vehicles to the line was where the latter crossed the lane to Sedgebrook Lodge Farm, and 65 was taken there early in 1966 (she arrived by the same route) in expectation of immediate removal by low-loader, but it was found that repairs were necessary, and the cab and saddle tank were removed. By this time all the track round her had been taken up — she finally left on 12th July 1966. *PITSFORD* was purchased by Mr E. E. Kimbell of the well known Northampton engineering firm, and she made history by travelling under her own steam from the BR sidings to the goods yard at Lamport level crossing, the last steam locomotive to work over this section of line. She was driven by her new owner.

By the spring of 1967 restoration was complete — the site levelled, all buildings removed; the locomotive shed and workshops first, followed by the weighhouse a few weeks later. Virtually all traces of the route were obliterated; even the concrete bridge under the main road was filled in and the parapets replaced by hedges and stone walls similar to their surroundings; many walls in this area have a look of the Peak District about them. The embankment carrying a section of the line across a natural hollow in the ground between the shed and the farm remained for a while, but was later removed. Hedges removed in the course of quarrying had been replaced by quickset (hawthorn), that by then had become part of the landscape; wooden fences were only used on the last replacements when the tramway was removed — the first hedge east of the shed: the point where the line passed by the farmyard: and east of the A508. In the farmyard itself are two buildings, one of wood and one of corrugated iron with iron-framed windows and curved roof, that look as if they might have come the quarry company, but this has not been confirmed. Pitsford had a good reputation for the excellence of its restoration while quarrying was progressing; topsoil removed by hand was returned to the worked-out ground within a few months. Now Pitsford was one of the first ironstone quarries to disappear almost completely under the bulldozer and earth scraper.

The final quarrying area was later developed by Peter Bennie Ltd for roadstone, all removal being by lorry. In the period May 1979 to January 1982 the Northampton Locomotive Group were permitted to store their metre-gauge Peckett locomotive (formerly Wellingborough Quarries) until they could find a more permanent home for her.

Grid References

737602	Junction with LMSR
738601	Locomotive shed
743668	Intermediate loop by Sedgefield Lodge Farm
749670	Bridge under main road

Locomotives

Gauge; 4ft. 8½in.

PITSFORD	0-6-0ST	OC	AE	1917	1923	15 x 20in.	3ft. 6in.	New 12/1923	(1)	
IRENE	0-6-0ST	IC	MW	1359	1896	15 x 22in.	3ft. 9in.		(a)	(2)
No. 2	0-4-0ST	OC	MW	345	1871	12 x 18in.	3ft. 0in.		(b)	Scr 1/1964
65	0-6-0ST	OC	HC	1631	1929	15 x 22in.	3ft. 4in.		(c)	(3)

(a) ex Pilton Quarries, Rutland c 1931.
(b) ex Park Gate Iron & Steel Co Ltd, Charwelton Quarries, c 1935
(c) ex Appleby-Frodingham Steel Co Ltd, 10/1957.

(1) to Midland Ironstone Co Ltd, Crosby, Lincolnshire c 9/1934; ret. c 1934. To E. E. Kimbell, Boughton 7/1966, then to W. McAlpine, Dobson's Farm, Fawley, Buckinghamshire.
(2) to Pilton Quarries c 1935 (?).
(3) to Midland Quarry, Crosby, 7/1966.

Gauge; 2ft. 0in.

PIXIE	0-4-0ST	OC	WB	2090	1919	6 x 9in.	1ft. 7in.	(a)	(1)

(a) ex Pilton Quarries c 6/1923; to Pilton 1928; ex Park Gate Iron & Steel Co Ltd, Eaton (Basic) Quarry, Leicestershire c 1933.

(1) to Cranford Ironstone Co Ltd 1949.

Pitsford Quarries. The final section of track waiting to be lifted, on 22nd May 1966, with small diesel crane in attendance. (V. J. Bradley)

Quarry Machines

No. 135	S. Stripping Shovel	RH	983*	1925	2¼ Cu.Yds.	75ft.	New 1/1925	Scr 1958
No. 4	D. Shovel	RH	1167	1927			(a)	(1)
No. 15	S. Navvy	RH	792	1923			(b)	Scr 1958
24RB	D. Shovel	RB	9434	1946	7/8 Cu.Yds.	18ft. 6in.	New 7/1946	(2)
490	E. Shovel	R&R	3075	1955	2½ Cu.Yds.	36ft.	New 11/1955	s/s
5W	E. Walking Dragline	RB	21407	1956	4 Cu.Yds.	135ft.	New 10/1956	(3)
43RB	D. Dragline	RB	18364	1954			(c)	s/s
21RB	D. Shovel	RB	2860	1935	3¼ Cu.Yd.	18ft. 6in.	(d)	(4)
No. 231	10RB D. Crane.Crawler							
		RB	4691	1939	5/6 Cu.Yds.	35ft.	(e)	(5)

(a) ex Lamport Quarries c 1932.
(b) ex Mitchell, Bros, Sons & Co Ltd 1933
(c) ex South Durham Steel & Iron Co Ltd, Irchester Quarries.
(d) ex Lamport Quarries c 1960.
(e) ex Cranford Quarries 1966.
* BSC records quotes 993 throughout.

(1) Ret. to Lamport Quarries.
(2) to Cranford Quarries c 1965.
(3) to Woolsthorpe Quarries late 1965.
(4) to Cranford Quarries c 1965.
(5) to Cranford Quarries 1966.

SPRATTON QUARRIES

Owners: Attenborough & Co: Attenborough & Timms from 1899.

The title of these quarries is a misnomer arising from the rather curious provision by the LNWR of two stations, Spratton and Brixworth, about half a mile apart on the line to Market Harborough, the villages served lying respectively west and east of the branch; the tramway from the pits (which lay just south of Brixworth village) ran down to a tipping stage a quarter mile south of Spratton station, though in fact the village of that name is a mile and a quarter away across the valley. The tramway was of the uncommon 4ft. 0in. gauge and probably dates from the opening of the quarries in 1873, though MS indicates that these were closed from 1875 to May 1877. The ground was leased from Lord Wantage — most of it anyway.

Precise details of equipment have not survived in memory but it may be assumed that they were similar to those obtaining at the sister line described below; the locomotive stock was transferred thither at the closure, and probably serviceable wagons also. The section from the level of the pits to the LNWR sidings was a double track cable-worked incline, while the upper level was presumably worked first by horses but from 1881 by locomotive. Quarrying took place on both sides of the Northampton road, doubtless commencing on the western side where the stone was outcropping, while the eastern quarries lay under overburden that increased up to nearly 20ft. The quarries are described as 'standing' in 1896/7 but then operating was resumed, the last record in LQ being for 1912, in which year the ground west of the road was leased to Staveley Coal & Iron Co Ltd. The history of the firm of Attenborough & Timms is given in some detail in the section on Brixworth Quarries, and the partnership appears to have been dissolved in 1913. The area east of the road was also leased by Staveley in 1918, reopened by them in 1939 and worked intermittently until 1949, as their Brixworth Quarry (see under Lamport Quarries section).

Scant traces of the main line sidings remain, and of the ironstone tramway only the broad outline of excavated fields is to be seen. The brick parapets of the bridge under the main road remain; the west side is of red brick with blue capstones oblong in section, and on the east side red brick with blue capstones triangular in section. The bridge has been filled in completely on the east side but not on the west, where the lower level of the surrounding ground tells its own tale. There is no smoke-blackening under the bridge, so possibly locomotives were not used on this eastern section. Under the private drive to Park Farm there was also a bridge, of which nothing remains; but the contours of the ground indicate clearly enough where it was—a ten-foot drop from the drive to the field, with an ironstone face each side. In 1977 an oak tree was standing on the site of the former bridge.

Grid References

735698	LNWR transfer
739699	Top of incline
742700	Bridge under Park Farm track
743701	Locomotive shed
748699	Bridge under main road

Locomotives

Gauge; 4ft. 0in.

SPRATTON No. 2	0-4-0ST	OC	HC	227	1881	7 x 12in.	2ft. 0in.	New 11/1881	(1)
LOUISA	0-4-0ST	OC	HE	298	1882	9 x 14in.	2ft. 8½in.	(a)	(1)

(a) ex Winstanley Colliery Co, Lancashire 5/1900.

(1) to Brixworth Quarries after 1980.

BRIXWORTH QUARRIES

Owner: Rev. C. F. Watkins

The earliest known workings at Brixworth were operated from 1863 by the Reverend Charles Frederick Watkins, Vicar of Brixworth; from 1870 the records give the name as 'Stonepit Close', which probably applied also to the earlier years. The vicar died in 1874. There just *might* be some connection with the quarries described below and operated by Attenborough & Co from 1873, but apart from the coincidence of date there is nothing to suggest this was so; Attenborough's lease was not with the Rev. Watkins. There is obvious evidence of quarrying between church and road, on ground now covered by allotments, and this is presumed to be Stonepit Close. Whether a tramway was used to connect the quarry to the LNWR is not known, but if so, it could have taken at its lower end the same course as the Sheepbridge line opened some ten years later.

Grid Reference

747713   Stonepit Close

BRIXWORTH QUARRIES

Owners: Sheepbridge Coal & Iron Co Ltd.

According to a Board Minute of 28th October 1880, the Sheepbridge company acquired a lease for working ironstone on ground formerly belonging to a Mr Eldred, but difficulties in implementing this were met, and negotiations for another lease were made with the Trustees of Roe's Charity, under the will of the late William Wood, the fields concerned lying close to the south side of the Brixworth-Cottesbrook road. The company minutes state that the lease was 'sealed' on 17th June 1882 and the term probably dated from 25th March 1882 for 14 years; the royalty, 7d per ton, was reduced to 4d in September 1886. The LNWR put in sidings at Brixworth station, where a tipping dock was built and a tramway of about 2ft. gauge laid therefrom to the quarries, passing beneath the road by a tunnel; Sheepbridge wrote to Brixworth Highways Board (see their papers in Northamptonshire Record Office) on 26th April 1883 of their desire to make the tunnel, and constructed the tramway in the summer and autumn of that year. The slope of the valley side is here steeper than north or south of the village, hence cable operation with a winding drum at the summit of the double incline was installed for hauling the wooden wagons.

Production commenced on 9th January 1884, as recorded in Brixworth parish registers, and passed to us by Geoffrey Starmer from one of his industrial archaeology class pupils; an unusual piece of information for such a source, but quarrying had been going on all round the church for the previous twenty years. Working continued to June 1896, the lease expiring on 25th March 1896; the company applied for an extension to work the residue of ore remaining and to restore the land, presumably only a matter of a few months. As the site was purely outcrop and quarries comparatively shallow, there are no very marked traces of the quarrying area, but sunken ground can be seen on both sides of the green lane west of the church, known as Lynch Lane. Most significant, perhaps, is the dip in the lane where 'The Lynch' adjoins it on the south side, beyond which the hedge between lane and field is clearly of more recent growth than the rest, or the more elevated hedge on the north side. Presumably the original section of hedge was removed so that the ironstone beneath Lynch Lane could be extracted, and the hedge then replaced. There is no trace of the bridge mentioned above, nor of the tramway route.

Grid References

738719	Tip to LNWR
744717	Tunnel under road
743713	'Dip' in 'The Lynch'

BRIXWORTH QUARRIES

Owners: Attenborough & Co: Attenborough & Timms from 1899: Brixworth Ironstone Co Ltd from 11th March 1909 (subsidiary of Clay Cross Co Ltd from 25th March 1928)

These quarries had much in common with the so-called Spratton quarries already described, in ownership, equipment and operating methods; but while Spratton was closed when the firm of Attenborough & Timms ceased trading in 1913, the Brixworth quarries remained in operation under new ownership, making them the most important of the four quarries in the immediate vicinity of Brixworth.

The field known as Home Close was leased by Joseph Edward Goode to Thomas Green, Thomas Pressland and Richard Attenborough for the extraction of ironstone, the lease being dated 24th June 1873 for 21 years; when Mr Goode died in 1877, the property passed to his brother, John Goode, with whom the partners enacted a new lease dated 10th September 1878. The lease empowered the partners to make 'roads or railroads or tramroads or sidings' as necessary for taking the ironstone, on which a royalty of 7d per ton was levied — a rather high figure for the time — and no calcining was to be carried out without prior consent. The partners listed presumably constituted the firm of Attenborough & Co, and Richard Attenborough is described as being 'of Reading, Berkshire', and in 1883 was attached to the firm of Stenson & Co of Reading (presumably connected with the Stenson & Co of St. James's End, Northampton). However, there was a Mrs H. Attenborough resident in Brixworth in 1874. Another curious point is that MS for 1873-75 quotes the owners as G. Attenborough & Co; maybe G. Attenborough was Richard's father, but his name does not appear on the lease — or it could be a clerical error in MS repeated for three years by simple copying. Finally, it may be noted that one of the partners was named Pressland; and a 'Presland's Pit' was amongst those worked by Lamport Ironstone Co — which see — and not by Brixworth.

Another lease in similar terms, also dated 24th June 1873 for 21 years, was made between Joseph Edward Goode and Mr John Becke, Thomas Green and Thomas Pressland for the fields known as Behind Church Close, Hollow Close, First Lodge Leys and North Lodge Leys, which formed a wedge-shaped piece of land running northwards from Home Close, which was adjacent to the church on the north side.

Richard Timms is quoted in one 1883 Directory as Attenborough's 'Agent or Manager', while another Directory for 1884 mentions Edward Coles as

'Agent and Contractor'. The Hudswell Clarke locomotives 212 and 227 were despatched to 'Edward Coles, Contractor', so it may be inferred that Coles had been commissioned to work the quarries and Timms to manage them for the proprietor; at this period there were a number of ironstone quarries being operated by contractors. By 1890 Richard Attenborough had moved to Northampton and by 1894 is quoted among the 'principal landowners' of Brixworth, having purchased the land from which he was then extracting ironstone. Richard Timms was taken into partnership in 1899, the firm becoming Attenborough & Timms; Richard Attenborough died on 19th May 1901, whereupon Timms assumed control and became the landowner also; he occupied the offices in George Road, Northampton, from which were also managed the other quarries owned by the firm. Timms was a leading Baptist in the area and described by Victor Hatley from a photograph as 'venerable looking and bearded'; he died in May 1922. These historical family details have only minor relevance to the ironstone quarries, but they serve to show that things are seldom as simple as they appear at first; as soon as one starts delving into the files, all sorts of anomalies, as well as confirmation, crop up, and some of these affect the history.[1]

The earliest workings were in the fields covered by the two 1873 leases, to the north of Brixworth's famous Saxon church, and were at the 400ft. contour; and to these was laid a tramway of the unusual 4ft. gauge, like its confrere at Spratton. At the lower terminus, at 250ft. above sea level, were a couple of railway sidings and a tippling dock with the staging across the line, so that end-tipping narrow gauge wagons could be emptied into standard gauge wagons standing beneath. The first half mile of tramway was perfectly straight, with an intermediate crossing loop, the lower half embanked and nearly level and the upper half in cutting and at successive gradients of 1 in 28, 20, 18, 23, beyond which the line curved south, still in cutting at 1 in 58, towards the quarries. The tramway was hedged on both sides — a rather unusual feature — and the rails were spiked directly to the sleepers in the normal way. At one time cable haulage was tried out on the most steeply graded portion at the upper end, and the rollers and other fittings survived right up to the closure; but its use was soon abandoned in favour of locomotive traction and the first known locomotive arrived in April 1879. The 1883 OS shows no locomotive shed however. When ground adjacent to the main road was opened up, the tramway cutting was extended in a south easterly direction, and a locomotive shed of slatted wood and corrugated iron roof — the latter possibly a later modification — built at the summit; the end wall and one side of

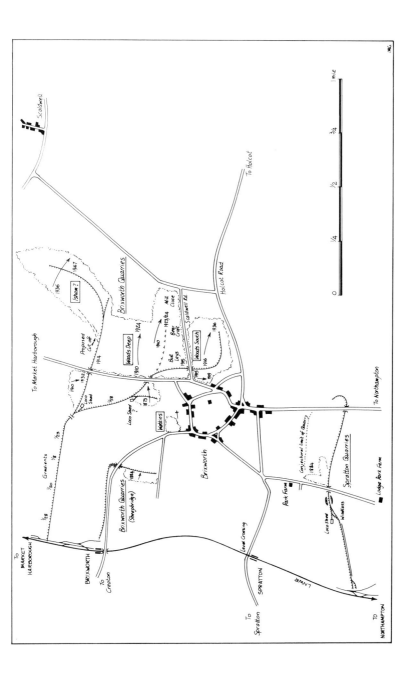

unmortared stone were against the cutting walls. A wooden overbridge crossed the line nearby for the convenience of the farmer.

The original leases were due to expire in 1894, and in the 1890s Richard Attenborough purchased four fields east of the Northampton-Market Harborough road, north of Scaldwell Road; these were Houghton Cross Close, Mill Close, Bear Croft and Bull Leys, and in 1906 Richard Timms purchased Butts Leys, alongside. The total area involved was 51 acres, and a tunnel was driven obliquely under the main road to enable the tramway to reach the area, which was probably worked in the last decade of the 19th century; the tunnel appears on the 1900 OS map. Working generally moved eastwards. In *Machinery Market* of 1st May 1899, the newly-formed partnership of Attenborough & Timms advertised for a 'good second hand locomotive, 4ft. gauge, to haul 40-50 tons', doubtless in connection with these extensions. *LOUISA* came the following year.

In 1908 Richard Timms negotiated the sale of the Brixworth quarries—'tramway, subway, locomotive, trolleys and other plant' and including 200 wagons to be selected by the purchaser; and on 11th March 1909 Brixworth Ironstone Co Ltd officially took over from Attenborough & Timms and commenced operations on a rather larger scale than the partners. A lease was negotiated with William Thomas Vere Wayte Wood of Brixworth for a term of 30 years from 25th March 1909, of nearly 375 acres, nearly all east of the main road; of this much the larger area lay north of the partners' freehold land, but there were also four fields south of Scaldwell Road where this ran due west to east from the main road. The royalty was set at 4d per ton. Brixworth Ironstone Co Ltd also purchased on 29th September 1929 two Windmill Closes, of just over two acres; this included the windmill, which seems to have disappeared during the subsequent quarrying operations.

Quarrying in this area commenced in 1910 in Woods Deep pit immediately east of the main road; this was worked clockwise from a short trailing branch to the main tramway. Working of the freehold area to the south continued over the same period. To facilitate the development of the new ground a branch tramway was constructed, leaving the existing line by the loco shed, passing under the main road by another brick tunnel (authorized by agreement with Northamptonshire County Council 27th April 1912) and then curving southwards to the Woods Deep pit area. Another small area, west of the main road and north of the tramway, was worked 1910-1913; the name of this quarry is not recorded but it could well have been Woods Shallow pit by comparison. Operations at Woods Deep pit slackened in the 1920s with the reduced demand, but continued to

1936 (see below). That part of the Wayte Wood lease south of Scaldwell Road was called Woods South pit, and the tramway was extended in 1915 across the worked-out area north of Scaldwell Road and beneath the latter via a brick arch; west of the tramway working was anticlockwise in the period 1915-19, and east of the tramway in strips from 1916 until abandonment in September 1932. The track was taken up about 1936. A condition of the Wayte Wood lease was restoration of the land to its original state after extraction of ironstone, but following a relaxation of this in respect of 15½ acres in 1921, the full restoration clause was rescinded as from 25th March 1928, with payment to the landowner in lieu. All that was required was to 'roughly level crowns or crests of the hillocks'. The eastern part of Woods Deep pit was planted with mixed trees, mostly larches and other conifers, in the late 1920s; this was on former 'hill and dale' workings.

Control of Brixworth Ironstone Co Ltd was acquired by the Clay Cross Co Ltd, to whom the Wayte Wood lease, and agreement for release from the restoration clause, were assigned as from 25th March 1928, i.e. with 31 years of the term of 50 years still to run. An inventory of the rail system made in 1929 gives the standard gauge lines at the tipping stage as totalling 433 yards, and the 4ft. gauge line as 4715 yards (just over 2½ miles), with 101 wooden 'trams' (including those in working order and parts of old trams) and a navvy. The last is not specified, but George Rowley, who was offered the job of driving her, tells us she was a long-jib 20 ton Ruston. The inventory does not mention locomotives; there was only one locomotive at the time of the 1908 inventory, but the locomotives from the Spratton quarries came to Brixworth, presumably soon after the closure of the former in 1913.

Because of the recession in industry, and the 'unsatisfactory state of the mines' Clay Cross decided to cease operations and on 26th March 1933 gave notice to the landowner to determine the lease as from 25th March 1934; but after negotiations Clay Cross decided to carry on, initially for a further five years, and then for a further term. On 9th October 1934 Clay Cross officially purchased the tramway and the freehold land of nearly 51 acres, representing some of the older quarrying area — Bull Leys, Bear Croft, Mill Close, Butts Leys, Windmill Close, Houghton Cross Close, to use the picturesque field names. Two small pieces of worked-out area east of the main road, west and east of the old southern tramway course, were sold to A. Hamson & Sons Ltd, builders and contractors of Brixworth, respectively on 24th November 1938 and 31st December 1943.

Working in Woods South pit had ceased in September 1932, but continued in Woods Deep pit (sometimes simply called Deep pit) to 1936;

the face probably also extended into the freehold area. In that year the northern part of the Wayte Wood lease was opened up, and the face was eventually lengthened to about half a mile, roughly parallel to the Brixworth-Scaldwell road to the east. In the interests of increased wartime production the Ministry of Supply allocated a 55RB electric dragline in 1940; the fate of the steam navvy is not recorded. Also in 1940 it was proposed to lay a 'cut-off' across a small portion of the Lamport estate to give easier tramway access to the new face; a wayleave was negotiated with Sir Vere Isham, the landowner, and with Staveley Coal & Iron Co Ltd, the lessees, for ten years from 25th March 1940, but the change was never implemented. The western limit of the lease was the meandering course of the parish boundary, and while Clay Cross was shovelling away the ground on the east, Staveley were equally busy on the west in their Isham South pit. The Scaldwell quarry blacksmith remarked that it was a pity Sir Gyles Isham (the then landlord) and Squire Wood did not get together and make things easier; but perhaps the parish boundary had to be left for legal purposes.

In common with most ironstone systems, Brixworth enjoyed a period of intensified activity during World War II, all the output deriving from the quarry just referred to. During this period it was the custom to have both locomotives in steam, each bringing down in succession trains of loaded wagons, and then combining forces, with one locomotive in front and one at the rear, to take the empties back to the quarry; a footplate trip with the exhaust fetching the leaves rattling down from the trees lining the cutting was an exhilarating experience, now alas but a memory. For some years before the end, the quarries were the oldest ironstone workings still in use, a fact which the staff were very proud to bring to the notice of visitors. One wonders what Richard Timms would have made of it all, had he been able to revisit the scene; one thing is certain — he would have had no difficulty in recognising his railway, which had changed hardly a jot in half a century! The railside hedges, the trees on the cutting walls, the larch plantation on old quarry workings, all combined to make this tramway one of the prettiest of them all, possessing an air of more leisured days, an impression heightened by the vintage locomotives and wagons.

The steam locomotives were tiny machines, considering the near standard gauge, and were obviously based on designs intended for use on gauges of 2 or 3ft., rather than standard gauge machines cut down; *LOUISA* was in fact built to the 3ft. gauge. They had very little in the way of cabs, and *LOUISA* with its stovepipe chimney was not very prepossessing; the Hudswell Clarke with its bell-mouthed copper-capped chimney was a nicer

Brixworth Quarries (Clay Cross). Hunslet locomotive *LOUISA* standing by the footbridge over the tramway near the locomotive shed. Note the dropped bufferbeam to suit the wagons. August 1936.   (G. Alliez/Courtesy B. D. Stoyel)

looking job and was painted light green lined black edged with yellow, the name being painted in yellow on the tank. She was sent to Blackwell's of Northampton for a rebuild in 1938, along with the sister locomotive, whose saddle tank (and change of number) she acquired. *LOUISA* was painted 'invisible green' and had red-backed nameplates. The petrol electric locomotive was one of several purchased by Clay Cross from the War Stores Disposals Board, and was very heavy on petrol consumption, but interesting as a (partly at least) home-made design. The wagons were square in section, of wood, with small wheels and dumb buffers; buffer beams of the locomotives were specially lowered to deal with them.

The 55RB dragline was in 1944 hired to Parker Construction Co Ltd for work on an opencast coal site, under the auspices of the Ministry of Supply (who were still the owners); she later returned to Brixworth. The quarries did not long survive World War II, after which demand dropped generally. Closure was being considered in January 1946 and at a meeting on 7th October 1946 between Colonel Jackson and Joe Holmes, the quarry manager, this policy was confirmed; the dragline was to make one more full cut at the face and would then be transferred to Bloxham quarries, which were to be reopened. The reasons given to Mr C. P. Bates (Wayte's Wood agent) in a letter dated 2nd November 1946, was that the reserves, at an extraction rate of 1000 tons per week (a low figure by postwar standards) would last seven years, but the equipment would not—the steam excavator was worn out and the dragline was inadequate for the increasing overburden; transport by narrow gauge tramway and locomotives or rope haulage (even at the end the latter was evidently still in the minds of the quarry people) with tipping was 'inefficient and uneconomical'. The alternative of re-equipping the system on modern lines, with a standard gauge tramway and a walking dragline in the quarry, was ruled out by the smallness of the area to be worked. Staveley were approached but showed no interest in taking over Brixworth as part of their Lamport system, which would not have been difficult; and Sheepbridge and Naylor Benzon declined also.

Mr F. Dickens, the weighbridge clerk, in a letter dated 1st November 1947 to Mr R. F. Childs, recorded 'the last day on which ironstone was gotten at Brixworth quarry was 4th October 1947'. A start on restoration of land and fences was made before the end of quarrying, according to Clay Cross estate records of 13th August 1947. The track was lifted and the equipment disposed of in January 1948, and though the ultimate fate of the

Brixworth Quarries (Clay Cross). Looking north are the sidings on the Northampton-Market Harborough line, showing the gate across the lifted track, the weight office, and the tipping dock of the Brixworth ironstone tramway. The ends of the embankment were later cut back to make a lorry road to the Lamport calcine bank. The steam in the background is from a Lamport locomotive, 5th March 1954.   (G. H. Starmer)

Brixworth Quarries (Clay Cross). Unrestored Woods South pit, 12th May 1965. Quarrying ceased here in 1932, but the ground was not restored, the operators making a payment to the landowners in lieu. This still obtained in the early 1980s but building on the site is likely in the near future.

(G. H. Starmer)

Brixworth Quarries (Clay Cross). The locomotive shed in January 1969. This building disappeared piecemeal over the years and no sign of it now remains. (P. Staughton)

locomotives is not in doubt, precise details are lacking; the frame and other parts of *LOUISA* were seen in Clay Cross yard in July 1947 and she was scrapped some six years later. Whether the last loads were handled by *BRIXWORTH No. 1* or by the petrol-electric locomotive is not known; the latter was sent to Clay Cross, where it came to grief in collision with a steam locomotive and was scrapped. *BRIXWORTH No. 1* was also sent to Clay Cross for scrap.

The Wayte Wood lease was determined on 25th March 1948, i.e. after 39 years of the 50 allowed and 20 since it had been made over to Clay Cross.

Brixworth Quarries (Clay Cross). Tramway embankment, looking uphill towards the quarries, 22nd September 1977. (Eric Tonks)

The trackbed west of the main road was sold in 1949 to two farmers whose land bordered the line. Most of the freehold land was sold to Squire Wood, The later bridge under the A508 was filled in (as the agreement with the County Council required), using spoil from old workings; the job was commenced in May 1950 but was not completed until February 1952, as not being urgent. Of the other bridges to Woods South, the main road one had been filled in before the war, but not that under Scaldwell Road. There was, however, no programme of restoration comparable to that at Pitsford and Scaldwell. Under the revised terms of the lease, Wayte Wood had accepted cash in lieu of restoration, and the ground was left rough. After 1950 such a situation was no longer permitted. This lack of restoration may not have pleased the County Council but it made the Brixworth quarry site a lot more interesting to the industrial archaeologist (a band unknown by that name in 1950) than, say, Scaldwell. The lower embanked portion of the tramway retained its hedges, with odd axles and wheels buried in them, and was used as a footpath by humans and as a windbreak by sheep; some sleepers were in position, traces of the passing loop could be seen, and there was even a goodly quantity of coal on the stage by the lower terminus, where the tipping dock was intact. Buried in the hedge here was a notice 'Beware of haulage ropes', suggesting perhaps that cable haulage was in use for longer than employees recalled. On the other hand, parts of the cutting contained impassable undergrowth, or the walls had fallen in. The locomotive shed, though very tumbledown, was used for storing farm machinery, and the nearby footbridge was still present. There was also a curious wooden footbridge spanning the old cutting east of the main road, where a public footpath crossed the line to Woods South pit; this was filled in in 1949 by A. Hamson & Son Ltd, who owned the land each side.

As usual, destruction of many of these features has occurred since the above notes were made in 1957. In March 1962 Brixworth Rural District Council applied for planning permission, which was granted, to use the 'old ironstone workings' as a tip for household refuse, a fate that has befallen so many quarries, particularly in Northamptonshire. In the Spring of 1968 a (very!) rough road was laid parallel to the BR line from Brixworth station yard to the calcine clamps of the closed Lamport system (see below), so that lorries could take away ore remaining there; and in the process the brick retaining wall of the Brixworth tipping dock was demolished and replaced by a slope, though the foundation brickwork remained. The old corrugated iron mess hut was still there, however. Meanwhile, the RDC were busy filling the old quarry site with rubbish.

In spite of the inevitable changes wrought by the elements and the hand of man, the Brixworth remains in 1983 were still a lot more satisfying to visit than most, thanks to the terms of the lease. The course of the main tramway from the tipping dock to the locomotive shed site is clear throughout and on the embanked portion is a path through the bushes—but only a gnome could now get through some parts unscathed! The flimsy remains of the office at the tipping dock lay at a crazy angle in 1977 but disappeared shortly afterwards, and the route passes through a thicket and then on to an open embankment. On the way may be seen some ironwork possibly from a wagon, and consisting of a rod connecting steel plates with coupling hooks. A little way beyond this the embankment has been pierced for a pipeline and beyond this becomes overgrown. At least one length of rail remains and several sleepers are in position. The locomotive shed, which Pete Staughton described in 1969 as 'very ramshackle' but still used for storing hay, had by 1977 succumbed, the roof and timbers collapsed into an untidy heap sprawling across the course of the line, but with the slab side and rear walls built on the cutting face intact. This remnant was obliterated when in the late 1970s G. Mabbutt & Sons Ltd, a local contractor under the authority of the Northamptonshire County Council Highways Department, completely filled in the course of the later line towards the A508, also the cutting just west of the shed yard. Crops now grow over the fields each side of the former cutting, which is no longer visible (except from the air, perhaps?); the course of the early line southwards towards Brixworth church is still unfilled however.

East of the bridge the cutting, opening into a pleasant glade carpeted with wild flowers, was roughly filled in 1985, destroying beauty and interest. On the right is a conifer plantation covering early hill-and-dale working, and straight ahead the entrance to Deep pit, now filled with refuse. An agreement with Squire Wood to plant other exhausted areas with trees was not implemented because of wartime difficulties, and then 'forgotten'. To the left of the cutting the final gullet of the 1936-47 workings, stretching about half a mile, was in 1977 practically untouched since Clay Cross abandoned the site thirty years before; but by 1983 the demands of the 'Brixworth Amenity Tip' have been filling in the southern end, leaving the northern part still as it was.

The approach to Wood South pit east of the A508 has been partly overrun by a new industrial estate, but between Scaldwell Road and Holcot Road the course of the line is partly in cutting and partly slightly embanked, and the quarry site unrestored. The quarry area immediately north of Scaldwell Road is recognisable by the lowered levels. The bridge remains in recent years were as follows:-

A508 northern (later)	West side; red brick surmounted by concrete of triangular section; existing in 1977 but replaced by a wooden fence by 1981. East side: brick with ironstone facing blocks, and ironstone chips on top.
A508 southern (older)	West side: As 508 northern, east side. East side: red brick with large blue capping bricks. Disappeared in industrial estate development by 1983.
Scaldwell Road	North side: missing. South side: red brick, heavily overgrown with ivy. Open tunnel portal beneath.

The straggling hedge of the parish boundary marks the start of the Wayte Wood lease, and quarrying appears to have commenced near there and moved eastwards; between the hedge and the remaining gullet the few hedges have been replaced by fences, while to the east the ground towards Scaldwell Road has not been touched. Finally, the graveyard extension north of Brixworth church is at a lower level than the churchyard itself, indicating the site of early quarrying activity in Home Close.

Footnote

1   I am indebted to Mr F. Dix for the biographical details from these sources: Whellan's *Northamptonshire* (1874); Kelly's Directories, 1890 to 1910; *Wright's Directory for Northamptonshire*, 1884; *Northampton Notes & Queries*, 1894; and personal contact with various people.

Grid References

738721	Tipping dock to LNWR
748719	Locomotive shed
748713	Home Close Quarry (by church)
750714	Bridge under main road (first)
751719	Bridge under main road (second)
753711	Bridge under Scaldwell Road
754723	Terminus in Isham Quarry (north)

Locomotives

Gauge; 4ft. 0in.

BRIXWORTH No. 1	0-4-0ST	OC	HCR	212	1879	7 x 12in.	2ft. 0in.	New 4/1879	(1)
BRIXWORTH No. 1	0-4-0ST	OC	HC	227	1881	7 x 12in.	2ft. 0in.	(a)	(2)
(BRIXWORTH No. 2 until 1938)									
LOUISA	0-4-0ST	OC	HE	298	1882	9 x 14in.	2ft. 8½in.	(a)	(3)
-	4wPE		Clay Cross		c1927			(b)	(4)

(a) ex Spratton Quarries after 1908.
(b) ex Bloxham Quarries, Oxfordshire c 1942.

(1) to Blackwell & Son, Cotton End, Northampton; parts used in reconstructing No. 2, 1938.
(2) to Clay Cross Ironworks for scrap c 1947.
(3) to Clay Cross Ironworks 1947; Scr c 1953.
(4) to Clay Cross Ironworks c 1947; Scr c 1947.

Quarry Machines

No. 20	S. Navvy. Long jib	RH or RP						(a)	s/s
55RB	E. Dragline	RB	5100	1940	1¾ Cu.Yds.	70ft.	New c 9/1940	(1)
							(b)	

(a) ex ?
(b) This machine was supplied new to Clay Cross Co Ltd, and is presumed to have been here.

(1) to Bloxham Quarries c 1948.

LAMPORT QUARRIES

Owners: Lamport Ironstone Co: Staveley Coal & Iron Co Ltd from c.1923: Staveley Iron & Chemical Co Ltd from 23rd September 1948: Staveley Minerals Ltd from 7th March 1961.

Two groups of quarries were developed simultaneously under the general heading of 'Lamport Quarries', one group at Hanging Houghton on the crest of the escarpment and the other at Scaldwell about a mile to the east. Initially ownership was loosely credited to Lamport Ironstone Company, but the negotiation of leases and wayleaves was conducted by the parent company, Staveley Coal & Iron Co Ltd; the latter frequently operated individual quarries through subsidiaries but in the present case the local title was soon dropped in favour of that of the principals. The Brixworth Ironstone Co Ltd, newly formed in 1909, leased in that year from the squire a large area of ground running from southeast of Brixworth to the northeast, where it abutted on the Scaldwell parish boundary; and in the following year George C. Bond (the name Bond runs like a thread through the history of ironstone quarrying for nearly fifty years) wrote to the vicar of Scaldwell, the Rev. K. Kershaw, 26th August 1910 concerning the possibility of acquiring some of the glebe land for working ironstone[1] Nothing seems to have come of this, however, and in 1912 the much more ambitious plans of Staveley ruled out any possibility of Brixworth Ironstone penetrating the area.

Amongst the Overstone Papers in the Northamptonshire Record Office are a set of letters written in March 1909, referring to the development of ironstone on the Lamport Estate and indicating that negotiations had started well before Staveley commenced operations. The date suggests that it was Brixworth Ironstone who were interested at the time, as the company was formed that month to take over from Attenborough & Timms, and acquired their Wayte Wood lease later in the month; but the letter of 1st March 1909 from a firm of solicitors to the estate states 'There seems to be considerable competition for the ironstone lying under the Lamport Estate' and recommending that a mining expert be consulted for advice.

A letter from Sir V. Isham, then at St. Leonards, of 16th March 1909 to 'Will' says 'I am trying to get the Company to accept a lease over about one hundred acres as a commencement. If this goes through, we will grant a wayleave to Wood of Brixworth, who wishes to work stone on this property that could only be got to the railway over my land. ½d per ton is the usual arrangement for this'. For the Lamport stone a royalty of 4d per ton was suggested. Later letters stated that ironstone had been proved over about three hundred acres, and there was probably more on the west side of the main road. It would appear from these fragments that Brixworth Ironstone and Staveley were both after ore in this area. Later, as we know, Brixworth opened up their pit between Scaldwell and Brixworth, but took the output via a new tunnel under the main road to their existing tramway, and not over Isham land; even a 'cut off' over the latter, proposed in 1940, was never implemented.

The lease with Sir Vere Isham was for 50 years from 25th March 1911 and covered an area of some 800 acres, including much of the parish of Hanging Houghton from the railway line eastwards, and in Scaldwell parish north and west of the village between the roads to Hanging Houghton, Lamport and Old. The royalty was 5d per ton and a wayleave of 1d was payable for minerals carried over the line from other estates. The other major lessor was Lady Wantage; Staveley had been examining the possibilities of leasing part of her estate as early as 1906 (see board minutes, 27th August 1906), but the lease was for 30 years from 1st July 1912, at a royalty of 4d and wayleave of ½d. The total area was about 1200 acres, mostly on each side of the Brixworth-Holcot road, but including also the Park Farm area southeast of Brixworth formerly occupied by Attenborough & Timms to serve their so-called 'Spratton Quarries'. According to LQ, the latter ceased to operate in 1912, when the lease was seemingly transferred to Staveley — who, however, never developed this area, as far as is known.

Lamport Quarries (Staveley). The aerial ropeway, looking west from the Northampton-Market Harborough road towards the BR line. Behind the centre pylon can be seen the water tank at the site of the locomotive shed of the former narrow gauge tramway serving the Hanging Houghton pits. 5th March 1954. (G. H. Starmer)

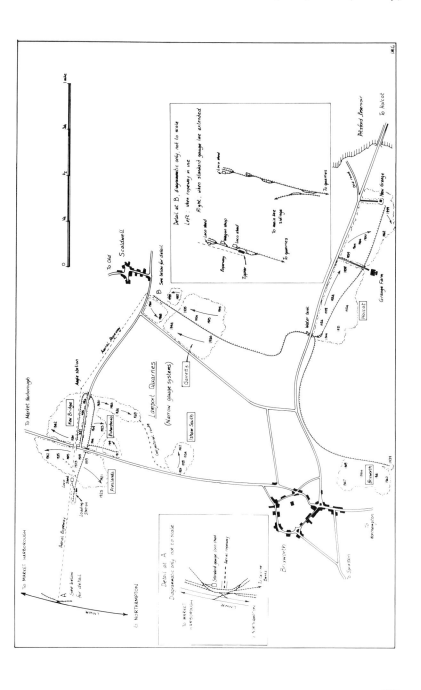

The Isham and Wantage leases were roughly a mile apart but were linked by leasing ground from Mary Ann Garrett (120 acres) and J. H. Mallard, both for 30 years from 1st July 1912. Mrs Garrett's land lay immediately west and southwest of Scaldwell village and carried a royalty of 4d for ironstone, with nil wayleave, but the Mallard land was used only to lay a tramway to reach the Wantage lease south of the Holcot road. The site of the old 'Spratton Pits' east of the main road was leased six years later, from 1st July 1918 for 24 years from a number of owners/occupiers; while a wayleave for 20 years with W. T. V. Wayte Wood was used to provide a tramway connection to that serving the Holcot area. It will be seen that the Staveley properties very effectively 'boxed in' the Brixworth Ironstone Co (later Clay Cross) quarries, preventing them from further expansion. All these leases were extended in time as required by circumstances.

We have already seen that as we move northwards from Northampton towards Market Harborough, the ironstone becomes progressively more elevated above the railway line in the Maidwell valley, hence direct rail connection between the quarries and the LNWR was not possible. A map attached to the Isham lease indicates that a rope-worked incline was first considered but instead a 3ft. gauge tramway system was introduced both here and on the Wantage lease, and the output of both taken away by a

Lamport Quarries (Staveley). The ropeway mechanism at Scaldwell, with the hauling engine house on the extreme left. Left to right are the office; ropeway angle station; loco shed; narrow gauge tramway over the chutes to the buckets; wagon sidings. (G. H. Starmer)

Lamport Quarries (Staveley). Mechanism as observed from the ropeway level, showing empty and full buckets. Tipping dock above, on left. 5th March 1958.   (G. H. Starmer)

Lamport Quarries (Staveley). Ropeway crossing on the Northampton-Market Harborough road, 5th March 1954, showing the girder structure to collect any material falling from the buckets.   (G. H. Starmer)

common aerial ropeway down to sidings alongside the LNWR between Brixworth and Lamport stations. It is interesting to note, however, that the original wayleave granted 9th October 1912 to Staveley Coal & Iron Co Ltd for obtaining access to the Scaldwell quarries site, via land belonging to Arthur Manning, states that 'the company can use either ropeway or rails' and the annexed plan shows the course of the alternatives—the ropeway on the line adopted and the tramway on a generally similar route but crossing the lane about half a mile from Scaldwell. This would have linked up with that at Hanging Houghton and the combined output then despatched by the ropeway from the one loading station. On the face of it this would seem a simpler arrangement than the one adopted, but possibly there were production advantages in being able to load from two stations at the same time.

The ropeway was built by the German firm of Adolf Bleichert at their Leipzig works and installed by British workmen under the supervision of a German foreman (who had to leave rather hurriedly a few days before the outbreak of World War I!). The ropeway was nearly two miles long and the carrier cable was supported on pylons about 400ft. apart and consisting of angle iron structures on concrete bases. The steel buckets which were set at the same spacing as the distance between each pair of pylons were 50 x 36 x 26in. deep, and had a nominal capacity of one ton, though 25 cwt. was often carried; a bridge was built where the ropeway crossed the Northampton-Market Harborough road to prevent possible damage from falling stone. At the loading and unloading stations and at the intermediate angle station, the buckets ran on rails, though still attached to the tractor cable; on the return trip they travelled upside down unless carrying coal to Scaldwell. The cable was examined by travelling seat every few weeks and the carrier cables were renewed every two or three years, the buckets being run on reception rails at Scaldwell.

On the narrow gauge line wooden side-tipping wagons were used and at the termini they were shunted on to elevated platforms so that the loads of ore could be discharged into a chute fitted with trapdoors at the foot, which were opened as ropeway buckets passed beneath them. In the case of Scaldwell, the train from the quarry by-passed the platform, for which the locomotive was too heavy, and the nine wagons were shunted back on to the loop,, afterwards being run in rakes of three by gravity over the hopper. The buckets were suspended by grooved wheel from the carrier cable, which was prevented from sagging by tensioning weights (cages of concrete blocks), whilst the tractor cable was clipped to the buckets lower down and driven by a 75hp Robey semi-portable steam engine (which

Lamport Quarries (Staveley). Unloading point from the ropeway at Lamport sidings, 1954. The dumpcars were then moved to the calcine bank for unloading, after which the ore was loaded into wagons for transit by BR. (G. H. Starmer)

retained its original boiler throughout) stationed at Scaldwell. Only alternate buckets were filled at Scaldwell, the remainder travelling empty to Hanging Houghton, where there was a manually-operated 'siding' where they could be diverted for filling, and then re-attached to the cable. At the lower (Lamport) end of the ropeway the contents were tipped directly into standard gauge wagons, for marshalling which a series of sidings were laid for operation by gravity, the empty wagons being allowed to run one at a time under the hopper and then into a reception siding for later collection by the main line 'pick-up'. The decision in 1933, on reopening after a five-year shut-down, to calcine the ore before railing to

Lamport Quarries (Staveley). At the Scaldwell terminus the 3ft. gauge wagons discharged their loads into the buckets of an aerial ropeway for transit to the main line. This 1954 photo shows the wooden chutes that stood over the buckets. The ropeway can be seen in the background. (G. H. Starmer)

Staveley made this system inoperative, and a locomotive was provided to propel the 'dumpcars' on to the elevated sidings alongside the calcining clamps; the dried ore was then loaded by steam crane into standard ore wagons. Entrance to the sidings was protected by a centrally-pivoted signal that was turned by the passage of a locomotive and thus revealed its presence to the next arrival.

Frost was the main enemy of the ropeway, where the ore (which always contained a proportion of water) would freeze to a solid mass that even the addition of salt or hot ashes would not always cure, because of the length of time the load was in the air; as a result, the buckets would not empty properly, and as the return cable was sometimes of a smaller diameter (1¼in. as compared with a 1¾in. for that carrying the loaded buckets) breaks in the cable could happen. Nevertheless, in spite of these difficulties, the Scaldwell ropeway was probably the most successful of the few constructed to carry ironstone, and worked for nearly forty years. An order was placed with Markham & Co Ltd of Chesterfield 14th February 1923 for 40 'cars for ropeway, to sample' — one of the German ones, doubtless.

The Hanging Houghton system was compact, with a number of separate quarries grouped round the road junction of the A508 (Northampton-Market Harborough) with the road to Scaldwell, none of the working faces being far away from the ropeway loading stage. Near the stage was a locomotive shed of green-painted corrugated iron, for one locomotive, with a water

Lamport Quarries (Staveley). The loading stage at Hanging Houghton. Wagons tipped their loads through the space in the landing to the buckets passing beneath. Because of the exposed hillside site, conifers were planted on the embankment as a windbreak. 1953.

(G. H. Starmer)

Lamport Quarries (Staveley). Narrow gauge locomotive shed, water tank and ropeway at Hanging Houghton. 1953. (G. H. Starmer)

tank — an old boiler — mounted on a steel framework. The tipping chutes were in an exposed position on the escarpment and (as in a few other similar cases, but by no means all!) the owners had the foresight to plant a grove of fir trees to provide a windbreak, making a picturesque spot from which to gaze over the valley. The nearest working area was Preslands pit, west of the main road, and quarrying commenced here in May 1913, the month that the two Peckett locomotives arrived. *LAMPORT* was here in later years and may well have spent all her earlier working life at Hanging Houghton, with *SCALDWELL* working the Holcot pit associated with the Scaldwell tramway. The one locomotive sufficed while the working faces were close to the ropeway, but as the distances increased it became necessary to provide an additional locomotive, and *BANSHEE* was transferred from Scaldwell by the familiar method of laying a length of track along the grass verge — fortunately quite wide here — and picking up the rear rails, and laying them in front of the locomotive for the next move.

The first cut in Presland's pit was in direct line between loading stage and road, then working fanwise south and west to the edge of the outcrop, which was reached in 1925; working northwards from the original cut commenced in 1923, then through to 1942 apart from a break in the Depression period, 1928-33. In the angle between the roads, east of the A508 and south of the Scaldwell road, was Richardson's pit, where in the course of time the workings covered ground north, east and south of Hanging Houghton Lodge, farmed by the Richardson family. A tunnel under the A508 immediately south of the road junction was evidently driven as soon as excavations permitted at Presland's pit on the west, as production at Richardson's commenced in 1914. The first cut was adjacent to the main road, as far as the drive to the Lodge, and in the following year another face was opened south of the drive, the tramway crossing the latter on the level, it is believed. By 1924 the working face had reached a point south east of the Lodge, with the parish boundary (the limit of the lease) a mere 200 yards away; between here and the main road the ground fell below the 400ft. contour in a small valley, and the tramway was extended in a half-mile arc to open up a new quarry to the south on the higher ground, commencing with a gullet near the main road in 1926. This pit, known as Isham South, was worked 1926-28; working was resumed here and at Richardson's pit in 1933 and continued on a small scale for four years, when both were closed.

A more interesting development was the New Bridge pit east of the A508 but north of the Scaldwell road and requiring, as the name implied, the construction of a new bridge under the latter to give tramway access. The bridge was a quarter of a mile from the road junction, and a narrow strip of ground adjacent to the Scaldwell road was worked in the period 1924-27. It was not until 1936 that operations were recommenced here, but the New Bridge pit was then the most important of the Hanging Houghton quarries and continued without interruption (apart from that occasioned by the change of tramway to standard gauge — see below) to the end of working; it was probably the reopening of New Bridge pit (when Richardson's, Presland's and Isham South were all working) that necessitated the transfer of *BANSHEE* to the Hanging Houghton system. Quarry machines used in this area are not precisely recorded, but at New Bridge a 460 diesel-electric machine came new for the commencement of quarrying and remained to the end of operations here; she was unusual in being a combined shovel and dragline but was used mainly as a shovel. Another unusual machine was a 43RB (No. 4383) with a seven-cylinder engine, but again it is not certain where she worked.

The Scaldwell system was quite different, with a long straggling tramway running southwards from the ropeway terminal to tunnel beneath the Brixworth-Holcot road and then turning to tap the ironstone on the south side, to a maximum distance from the stage of about two miles. Scaldwell was the headquarters of the system and, strung alongside the line at the terminus of the ropeway, were the offices, locomotive sheds and workshops, among them a wagon shop where a full-time carpenter, Stan Manning, was employed in building and servicing wagons from the

Lamport Quarries (Staveley). 3ft. gauge *SCALDWELL* standing with train at Holcot pit on 25th February 1957. Note that the track is on top of the ironstone face. Loading shovel to left, 43RB dragline for removing overburden to right.　　　　(S. A. Leleux)

commencement of working; apart from a few made by an outside contractor when the line was opened, all the wagons of the two tramways were constructed in this tiny shop.

It was at the most distant point, at the end of the tramway, that quarrying commenced — on 3rd March 1914, according to the survey map — doubtless because the stone was practically outcrop here, where the ground sloped down to the site, later, of Pitsford Reservoir. This was known as Holcot or Wantage pit, the ground being leased from Lady Wantage. Starting at the western end, the ground was excavated in strips roughly at right angles to the road, and an excavator, locally called 'The Iron Man', was used to remove the overburden as work progressed. Ruston & Hornsby supplied a No. 20 long-jib steam navvy in 1920 and this was probably the one referred to; loading of ironstone was by hand in the early days, as was common practice. A combined shovel and dragline from Charwelton quarries came here in the middle 1930s, and was used up to World War II, and a combined shovel and grab was borrowed from Sproxton quarries in Leicestershire. On the tramway *SCALDWELL* arrived in May 1913 and was in sole charge until the arrival of *BANSHEE* in the middle 1920s. Where the line passed beneath the Brixworth-Holcot road a water supply was provided, and, south of the bridge, a runround loop, beyond which it was normal for locomotives to propel the trains the remaining distance to the working face. As at Hanging Houghton, there was a break in production from 1928 to 1933, when it seems that the whole Lamport system was closed down. The trackway to Grange Farm was reached in 1937, and the tramway — then in cutting on the lower slopes of the hill — was carried beneath by a tunnel of ironstone blocks and with a wooden parapet; in the course of time the cutting became lined with trees, which with the bridge made a picturesque spot. In 1935 a 21RB diesel excavator was supplied to Holcot pit. There was a break in quarrying here in the early war years, but by 1944 was in full swing again. On the tramway, *BANSHEE* had been transferred to Hanging Houghton to help at New Bridge pit, but had been replaced at Scaldwell by *HANDYMAN. BANSHEE* returned on the closure of Presland's pit and in 1944 all three locomotives — *SCALDWELL, BANSHEE* and *HANDYMAN* — were in steam daily, two working at the Holcot quarries and the third shunting at the ropeway terminal.

Another interesting development, provided for by the leases of 1918, but not put into effect until required by wartime demand, was the reopening of the area southeast of Brixworth formerly worked by Attenborough & Timms as 'Spratton Quarries'. A branch nearly a mile long was laid from the Holcot road bridge, running westwards, roughly parallel with the road, to the quarrying area; working took place from southeast to north in 1939-41, using the 20 ton long-jib steam shovel, then intermittently up to 1949. The track was taken up in 1950 but one fence was left in at the request of the farmer.

There were also small quarrying areas on both sides of the tramway between the ropeway terminal and the Holcot road bridge; on the east side there was quarrying 1915-21, resumed in 1934 and carried on until 1944, but from 1936 most of the ore came from the west side of the line, in Garrett's pit. According to Tom Leak, the transporter obtained from Kettering quarries worked here, and so probably did the No. 8 shovel from the same source. The branches in these pits were short in length. Track was of the usual flat-bottomed type, of 56 or 60 pound rail spiked directly to wooden sleepers on earth ballast, and the line was practically level as far as the Holcot road bridge. As with many quarrying operations, there were a number of archaeological finds. During the General Strike of 1926, Henry George, harvesting a field near the quarry, noted on the side of the tramway cutting a dark patch that proved to be wood ash and slag of an early, probably Roman, kiln; the sides were lined with stones, discoloured by heat. Mr Taylor, the quarry manager, said that the men had seen several such ovens in the course of opening up the working faces, but took no special notice of them. (See *Northampton Independent*, 4th September 1926).

Increased production was also required at Hanging Houghton during the war years, but this was accomplished in a more dramatic manner; instead of extending the narrow gauge, it was replaced by a standard gauge line

Lamport Quarries (Staveley). *LAMPORT No. 3* with loaded dumpcars beginning the long descent to the BR sidings on 26th March 1956. Note the safety net under the aerial ropeway from Scaldwell.

(G. H. Starmer)

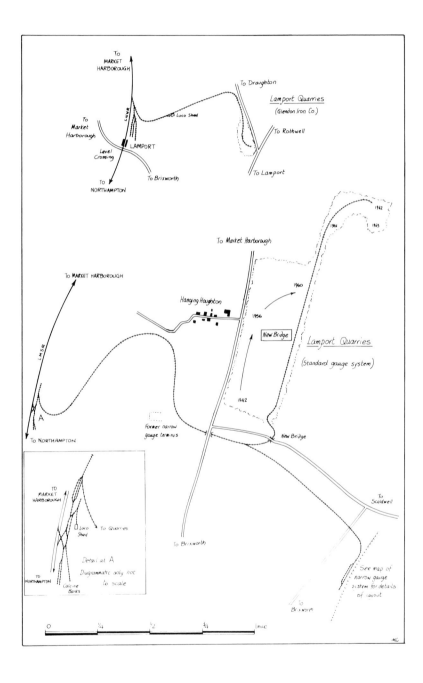

making direct contact with the sidings via a sweeping curve up the hillside to ease the gradient, which was nevertheless the steep one of 1 in 44. The line was an excellent piece of engineering carried out by Italian prisoners-of-war labour under the direction of Mr W. J. Davenport, the area manager of the Staveley group, and consisted of chaired track mostly on concrete sleepers on slag dust ballast; other ballast was tried but proved unsatisfactory. There were some sleepers of wood and a few of steel; the chairs were supplied by Armitage & Sons. There was a 'stop' board at the junction with the sidings, and a short way beyond this the line was carried on a stone embankment. The deep cutting at the top of the bank cut through the course of the narrow gauge line. An indirect consequence of the installation of the line was extra work at the calcine clamps; before its inception, the coal for calcining had been tipped into a hopper at the foot of the unloading (or 'tail') station of the ropeway, and a bucket elevator took the coal to the hopper and fed in the coal so that the resulting mixture in the dumpcar was correct for burning on the clamps. When some of the ore was brought down by rail, this system could no longer be used and recourse had to be made to the usual method of alternate layers of coal and ore. The only quarry operated by the standard gauge line was New Bridge pit, Presland's

Lamport Quarries (Staveley). *LAMPORT* and train at the tipping dock on 20th April 1961, with dumpcars on the lower line. (Ivo Peters)

having ceased in 1942. The new line utilized the same two bridges, suitably widened, but operations at the quarry were on a bigger scale. Three new machines were ordered from Ruston Bucyrus, and delivered in 1942; a 43B diesel dragline, fitted with a special bucket, used on the calcine bank and the others—a 55RB electric dragline and 43B diesel excavator—probably in the pit.

A more ambitious plan to convert the whole rail system to standard gauge was not carried through, probably because of wartime shortages, but was partially implemented some ten years later by putting in an extension of the line from Hanging Houghton to Scaldwell, with the aim of cutting out the ropeway, but continuing to use the narrow gauge as a feeder. Agreement with Northamptonshire County Council to cross the road running south from Scaldwell was given 30th November 1953, and the line was built in 1954. The ropeway was stopped in September 1954 and the men employed on it used in track-laying on the new extension, which was completed in January 1955; in the interim the Scaldwell pits were idle. The new line was of chaired track laid partly on secondhand wood sleepers and partly on concrete ones; at its terminus it paralleled the narrow gauge but much below it so that the side-tipping wagons could discharge their contents via a metal chute in the retaining wall into railway wagons below. The closure of the ropeway extinguished the picturesquely-named callings of 'pokers' (who cleared the chutes of ore when filling buckets) and 'shiners' (who were responsible for seeing the cable was kept thoroughly oiled from a travelling oil carrier).

The new system entailed a change in the operation of the narrow gauge line at Scaldwell. When the ropeway was operating, a train of nine wagons

Lamport Quarries (Staveley). One of the Bagnall locomotives bringing up a train of empty dumpcars for loading from the narrow gauge (right foreground). July 1962.

(G. P. Roberts)

Lamport Quarries (Staveley). In later years the ropeway was replaced by a long extension to the standard gauge line and the narrow gauge wagons tipped their contents into dumpcars at the lower level. The wagons tipped the other way from that used for the ropeway. Note how the wheels were clamped to prevent overturning. 7th September 1961.

(S. A. Leleux)

was hauled around the ropeway bunkers (not over the bunker staging, as the locomotive was too heavy) and the wagons were run back by gravity over the hopper to be emptied; they were then run down into the loop to form the next train, the locomotive having meanwhile collected the previous rake and set off towards the pits. When the standard gauge line was extended, the transfer point was further from the terminus and the level of the narrow gauge was raised slightly, and a loop was provided which ran on the concrete retaining wall well above the standard gauge line. A train from the pits would by-pass the chute, and the locomotive would then reverse and push the wagons so that they could discharge their loads via the metal chute; wagons were prevented from overturning in the process by steel bars fixed to the foundations of the dock and swung into position between the spokes of the wagon wheels, thus clamping them to the rails. The wagons were moved by the locomotive, which then propelled the completed train to the pits; the runround loop by the Holcot road bridge was not used. It may be noted that the wagons tipped to the east to empty into the ropeway buckets, but to the west to empty into standard gauge wagons; so in late 1954 all had to be reversed.

Lamport Quarries (Staveley). *ROBERT* with loaded train from Scaldwell pauses at the level crossing of the road to Brixworth. 5th August 1959.
(G. H. Starmer)

In the late 1950s and up to early 1961 the Lamport system was at its most productive, and output roughly trebled that obtainable from ropeway operation, which imposed its own maximum irrespective of rail improvements. The narrow gauge line had its share of these; in 1958 there were modifications to the layout at Scaldwell, including an extension to the locomotive shed (in the course of which the water tank was moved from the front to the west side) so that it could hold two locos instead of one, and *HANDYMAN* was given a somewhat leisurely overhaul, with the aim of using her for double-heading trains out of Holcot pit, which was now about 50ft. below track level at the bridge under the road. Even so, it was recognised that the life of the narrow gauge was limited, and it was not expected to last beyond 1963/64, as the reserves of the Holcot pit were nearing the end and, furthermore, the filling of the new Pitsford Reservoir was having its effect in making the stone very wet; indeed, the distance of the working face from the shore of the reservoir was only about 200 yards. In the Spring of 1961 the Holcot quarry was long, deep and wet, with the excavator bucket pouring water at every 'bite' — 'rather like working on a beach' it was described. As a result, the final working face was taken up the hillside a little.

Lamport Quarries (Staveley). *SCALDWELL* waits as the dragline fills the last wagon at Holcot pit, July 1962, then very near the end of operations here. Note Pitsford reservoir in the background. The stone here was often very wet; not surprisingly!　　　　　(G. P. Roberts)

The furthest point reached by the narrow gauge south of the Holcot road was New Grange, quarried in 1958; it was intended to work the ironstone over a considerable area of ground north of this road on Isham Charity land, but this would not be served by narrow gauge; verbal information at the time quoted the alternatives of extending the standard gauge about a quarter of a mile, or using lorries to bring the output to the existing tipping dock, modified as required. Since the 'North Pits', as they were being called, were never opened, the question of their operation is academic, but it may be noted that in 1961 management of the system passed to Staveley Minerals Ltd, a Stewarts & Lloyds subsidiary; and S & L Minerals Ltd had for some years been eradicating the narrow gauge generally. In this year instructions were given that no further major overhauls were to be given the two Peckett locomotives.

Economic considerations soon extinguished hopes of expansion of any kind. The narrow gauge was out of use in the early autumn of 1961 and, though working was resumed a year later, the staff were on a four-day week and the locomotive working Mondays and Tuesdays only; with Holwell Ironworks closed in September 1962 and Staveley on minimum production, output was down to 1500 tons per week, with Scaldwell (narrow gauge) and Hanging Houghton (standard gauge) quarries providing about 50% each. All this was being piled on the 'cally bank' by the BR line, and in the end the stocks of calcined ore were of the order of 200,000 tons.

The known locomotives were basically of the makers' standard designs, with no rarities; but few industrial locomotives pass their lives without acquiring some individual characteristics — which is what makes the study of them so fascinating — and they need to be described on that basis. On the narrow gauge, however, there was one mystery locomotive of German origin that arrived during the constructional period, doubtless imported by (and perhaps the sole property of) the contractors installing the ropeway. Unfortunately no details are recalled except that it was named something like *BOOMER* (a phonetic rendering); probably she returned to Germany on completion of the contract.

The first locomotives on the production site were two Peckett saddle tanks of characteristic neat outline, named *LAMPORT* and *SCALDWELL*: they bore the makers' standard livery of mid green lined black edged yellow with red valances, and had plenty of brass and copper embellishments — brass dome, copper chimney cap, brass nameplates and cab window surrounds, all kept brightly polished. The coupling rods, buffer beams and nameplate backgrounds were red. In 1953 *LAMPORT* was repainted plain green of a lighter shade and *SCALDWELL* a year or two later,

Lamport Quarries (Staveley). *LAMPORT* approaching the tipping dock area c July 1960. Note the familiar Lombardy poplar trees. (G. D. King)

Lamport Quarries (Staveley). *SCALDWELL* trundles through the snow towards the pits on 26th February 1958. (G. H. Starmer)

Lamport Quarries (Staveley). No complete photograph of *BANSHEE* appears to have survived, but her saddle tank remained in the bushes by the lineside for many years; as here, on 5th July 1953. (G. H. Starmer)

but both were still kept immaculately. *LAMPORT* worked at Hanging Houghton, *SCALDWELL* at Scaldwell; during the threat of invasion in World War II the nameplates were covered by iron sheets lest German paratroopers should learn their whereabouts too easily! Upon the closure of the Hanging Houghton narrow gauge system *LAMPORT* was repaired in its shed by Italian prisoners-of-war labour and transferred to Scaldwell.

Later locomotives were secondhand. *BANSHEE* arrived from Eastwell quarries probably in the mid-1920s and was transferred to Hanging Houghton, as already mentioned, but later (probably from the outbreak of war) returned to Scaldwell, when the Scaldwell system was worked intensively; but in 1944 she was replaced by *LAMPORT. BANSHEE* had a livery of green with black lining. Soon after *LAMPORT's* arrival, she was dismantled and, after lying about for some years, the frame, cab and boiler went to Loddington, but the saddle tank complete with nameplates remained in the lineside hedge near the tipping dock.

The Hudswell Clarke, *HANDYMAN*, had suffered a number of modifications—not all for the best, photogenically speaking. Like *BANSHEE*, she originated at Burton Latimer quarries, but was transferred to Cranford; adjustments to the tyres to enable her to work on the metre gauge line were not very successful, and for most of her stay she was stored in an isolated shed with the front exposed to the elements. By the time she had arrived at Scaldwell, she had acquired a somewhat crude smokebox and a stovepipe chimney. An undated photograph of her on a low-loader in Blackwell's yard at Northampton repainted black or dark green, strongly suggests that she received these modifications at Blackwell's before being transferred to Scaldwell. She did not receive much better treatment there,

Lamport Quarries (Staveley). *HANDYMAN* in Blackwell's yard, Ransome Road, Northampton. The date of the photo is not known but most likely is 1936, on its way to Scaldwell quarries. The locomotive had lain out of use at Cranford for about 17 years, so would need some attention; the most obvious being the exchange of the standard chimney with cast iron top to a stovepipe. (Collection G. H. Starmer)

Lamport Quarries (Staveley). *HANDYMAN* at Scaldwell on 25th July 1949. Although always known by this odd name, the locomotive only carried it a comparatively short time. No one knows why it was bestowed. (K. Cooper/IRS Collection)

however; there was originally a shed for one locomotive at the terminus, then another wooden shed was built near the tipping stage, but when there were three locomotives it was usually *HANDYMAN* that was left outside. When the main shed was extended, the two Pecketts used it and *HANDYMAN* occupied the wooden shed. During the war she worked along with *SCALDWELL* and *BANSHEE*, and at that time had a plain grey livery with the name in red paint on the tank, and with red coupling rods; in 1953 she was repainted plain green (without the name) and with red coupling rods.

With only the Holcot quarry being operated in the 1950s, one locomotive sufficed, but as the quarry became deeper it became necessary to divide the nine-wagon train; in 1960 *LAMPORT* could take four wagons up to the turnout by the bridge, then return for the others. To alleviate the situation, *HANDYMAN* was put back into service, having had a leisurely overhaul (but no repaint) since 1958. In early 1961 *LAMPORT* and *HANDYMAN* were both at work; first, *HANDYMAN* was used for pulling wagons, four or five at a time, from the pit to the turnout, where *LAMPORT* took over for the rest of the journey; later, both locomotives worked the whole way. But more often than not *LAMPORT* ended up pushing the lot up the final bank to the tipping dock. *HANDYMAN* thereupon returned to its shed and remained there until the closure. As stated, one Peckett was in use at this period, *SCALDWELL* up to early 1959, then *LAMPORT* to 1961, and *SCALDWELL* again from early 1962 onwards, by which time instructions had been given that no more major repairs were to be carried out on narrow gauge locomotives; the projected repairs on *LAMPORT* were therefore never done and she remained in a partially dismantled state to the end.

The standard wagons were conventional timber side-tippers carrying about five tons of ore—rather larger than usual, possibly because of the comparatively late date of the quarries. They were all built in the Scaldwell carpenter's shop by Stan Manning. The main frames were of 9in. by 7in. oak timbers running the full length of the wagon to form dumb buffers, the upper body of 2in. thick elm boards on cast iron ties and angles; for unloading the body was tipped sideways on a curved runner, a slight push being sufficient to overturn the load, at other times the body being held in place by hooks on the sub-frame. The wheels were cast iron and the axles ran in simple pedestal bearings without lubrication. There were no springs or brakes; if required, wagons were braked by 'spragging', i.e. inserting a wooden block through the wheel spokes to jam beneath the frames. Three link and hook couplings were fitted, and the wagons were unpainted and unnumbered. They were identical in pattern but differed slightly in

Lamport Quarries (Staveley). When the direct standard gauge connection was put in to New Bridge pit, the ropeway was no longer required. The new line cut across the embankment where the buckets had been loaded and a number of wagons were marooned at the terminus. They gradually fell to pieces over the years. 10th October 1961. (S. A. Leleux)

dimensions, as might be expected; samples measured were 8ft. 9in. by 5ft. 6in. by 2ft. 8in. and 8ft. 6in. by 6ft. 0in. by 2ft. 2in. deep. The total overall length was 10ft. 6in., and the wheelbase was 4ft. 10in. At Scaldwell the normal complement was 27 in three rakes of nine, i.e. two working sets and one spare. There had been some older wagons, somewhat smaller, with bodies 6ft. by 4ft. by 2ft., and a shorter wheelbase, and two of these were still out of use near Grange Farm as late as 1961.

When the standard gauge line was laid at Hanging Houghton, it cut through the narrow gauge terminal embankment, isolating there the remaining wagon stock, which was simply abandoned to encroaching undergrowth, but could still be reached by a somewhat perilous scramble along the wooden footboards over the tipping chute. 'Frozen' as they were for twenty years, the wagons exhibited more variety than those at Scaldwell, where discarded stock was presumably scrapped; most of them were the same as at Scaldwell, but there were two end-tippers with bodies 5ft. 2in. by 4ft. 5in. by 1ft. 10in., believed to have been used in constructing the embankment here; a standard wagon supplied by McLachlan & Co of Darlington (per plate); and a curious 'bogie bolster' wagon consisting of rolled steel joists 16ft. 4in. long, 3ft. 3½in. wide and 12in. deep, and carried on wooden bogies 4ft. 8in. wide, 6ft. 0in. long and with 3ft. 2in. wheelbase. This was built about 1936 to carry the jib of the No. 4 excavator, which was later transferred to Cranford. The wagons numbered about twenty at first, but over the years bits and pieces were filched to patch up those at Scaldwell and in the end only a dozen were left for the scrapman.

On the standard gauge *ROBERT* was in sole charge at the exchange sidings until 1942 — a six-coupled Avonside of conventional sturdy build but unusual in having chromium plated nameplates and maker's plates; this embellishment was specified when the locomotive was ordered but was fortunately not extended to the copper-capped chimney! The livery was green, lined black edged with yellow. When the new standard gauge line was opened to Hanging Houghton in 1942 the Ministry of Supply provided two locomotives of a series built by Bagnalls for ironstone traffic and finished in their normal livery of green with black lining edged with yellow (inside) and red (outside); this livery was applied to *ROBERT* also. In the course of a repaint in the early 1960s *LAMPORT No. 2* appeared in a rather darker green and with the red and yellow edging reversed with respect to the black line. The sight and sound of these engines taking the empties uphill would delight any steam enthusiast. When the standard gauge was extended to Scaldwell, the locomotives were about at the limit imposed by one tankful of water, so had the proposed extension to the 'North Pits' come about, provision of a water supply would have been essential; there was one for the narrow gauge by the Holcot road bridge, it will be remembered.

In the summer of 1961 *LAMPORT No. 3* was taken up the line to the junction with the branch to Hanging Houghton and the boiler was removed

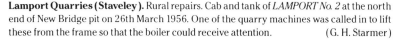

Lamport Quarries (Staveley). Rural repairs. Cab and tank of *LAMPORT No. 2* at the north end of New Bridge pit on 26th March 1956. One of the quarry machines was called in to lift these from the frame so that the boiler could receive attention. (G. H. Starmer)

Lamport Quarries (Staveley). *HARTINGTON* came from Staveley works as a replacement for *LAMPORT No. 3* when undergoing heavy overhaul, but she did not do much work, and her grubby condition made her look out of place. 7th August 1964.

(H. A. Gamble)

with the help of the dragline; it was sent away to William Elliott & Sons Ltd of Nottingham for a new firebox to be fitted and was returned early in 1962. As a replacement *HARTINGTON* (another Avonside) was sent from Staveley ironworks, her grubby black livery contrasting sharply with the smart turnout of the others, but she did not do much work; for one thing, she was restricted to shunting standard railway wagons at the exchange sidings, as she had not the centre couplings with which the other locomotives were fitted. These centre automatic couplings were for handling steel dumpcars in which ore was taken from the quarry face to the calcining clamps; the dumpcars were supplied by Midland Railway Carriage Wagon & Finance Co Ltd in 1933 and the body was a side-tipper normally kept in position by chains.

The closure of Lamport quarries, unlike Pitsford, was a long drawn-out affair. In the first place there were two sets of quarries served by narrow gauge and standard gauge lines, and (more importantly) there were, down by the exchange sidings something like 200,000 tons of accumulated calcined ore, removal of which was still being desultorily carried out fourteen years after the quarries themselves had ceased production. In this period a visit to the site might be rewarded by the sight of *LAMPORT No. 3* charging along with wagons of calcine—or the whole place silent and deserted, the

Lamport Quarries (Staveley). When quarrying ceased in 1963 there was a substantial stockpile of calcined ore at Lamport sidings. This was taken away as demand occurred. *LAMPORT No. 3* was the usual performer on these occasions, as here on 17th March 1966. Loading by 10RB digger.

(G. H. Starmer)

engines covered in bird droppings and weeds creeping over the rails. But at best it was only a pale shadow of the Lamport system proper, which had so much to interest the enquirer.

Production ceased on the narrow gauge 18th December 1962, and track lifting commenced at the Holcot quarry end in April 1963, with a few of the staff retained for this task, which continued throughout the year. It was, however, held up for a short time in the summer until a trip for enthusiasts had taken place on 17th August 1963, organised by the Birmingham Locomotive Club, though most of the hundred or so participants were Industrial Railway Society members. *SCALDWELL* took a train of wagons to the end of track just short of the Holcot road bridge, and *HANDYMAN* and *LAMPORT* were polished up and pulled outside for the photographers. Also present were a representative of the *Evening Telegraph* and Mr Lyall, assistant curator of Kettering Museum, who selected for preservation the best of the remaining wagons, plus four lengths of 15ft. rail. As with all such events, one's feelings were a curious mixture of elation from the experience and regret that it was unrepeatable. Railway preservation was established by then of course and the Talyllyn Railway purchased 1000 yards of track; 75 tons of rail went to Hoveringham Gravel Co Ltd but some was also cut up on the spot and sent to Corby as scrap. *SCALDWELL* was out tracklifting in September but by Christmas all the track had been pulled up as far as the locomotive shed, where she and *HANDYMAN* were stored, *LAMPORT* being left outside with a few remaining wagons.

During the summer of 1963 also the narrow gauge remains at Hanging Houghton, undisturbed for twenty years, were summarily dealt with; wagons were cut up, trees cut down, the tipping bunkers dismantled, and embankment smoothed over. Even the old quarry sites, pleasant spots to wander round and muse over, were levelled and restored to cultivation, slightly below road level. The same applied to the former Scaldwell quarrying area south of the Holcot lane, where all one could see from the bridge parapets was waving corn, with no hint of a cutting. The route towards Scaldwell was bulldozed and shoved about beyond recognition; the bosky area by the 'kink' in the line was ignominiously uprooted and swallowed up in the surrounding fields. *LAMPORT* was cut up on the spot, but one nameplate — hidden under a trapdoor in the stores for safety — went very properly to Roger West, whose observations have provided so much information in the above account. Happily, the other two locomotives went to preservation, also a further wagon to Brockham narrow gauge museum. The locomotive shed was acquired by Crawshaw Robbins & Co Ltd, contractors of Scaldwell, who rebuilt it for their own use, and they also took over the office and workshops. By the end of 1965 the only quarry reminder was an excavator and some odd plant stored on ground across the road from the office area, by the site of the old ropeway angle station; and there were two derelict wagons under the earth near Grange Farm, should archaeologists care to look!

We have dwelt at length on the narrow gauge tramway system, because of its intrinsic interest, but from the production point of view the standard gauge was the more important, and at the end of the 1950s quarrying had extended alongside the east side of the A508, well past Hanging Houghton. In 1961 a gullet was driven as far as the Lamport-Old road, and quarrying commenced on the south side of this opposite Faxton Grange, working clockwise, i.e. southward. Agreement had also been reached with the County Council to cross the road at the point in line with the initial gullet, to tap ground to the north; but the plan was never implemented, as production ceased 3rd April 1963. Restoration here was more protracted, the track being lifted at the quarry end in the ensuing twelve months, and down to the junction with the exchange sidings by the autumn of 1964. In January 1965 a dragline was busy filling the cuttings at Hanging Houghton, leaving in the end the same scene as on the narrow gauge — bridge parapets, pasture and cultivated fields on the quarry site.

Meanwhile, down at the exchange sidings efforts were being made to get rid of the mountain of calcined ore, not very successfully. In 1963 the demand was almost non-existent, and some of the ore was said to be incorrectly 'burnt'; to rectify this, a further layer of coal was laid down in June 1963 but was removed two months later, with no further calcining done. Still, it was being sold to Bilston from time to time, *LAMPORT No. 3* doing the work. She had at one time the reputation of being 'a bad engine' — one of those apocryphal tales, no doubt — but was improved after the boiler overhaul of 1962. It was then thought that economies might be effected by using a diesel locomotive instead, and in December 1965 the Fowler diesel *DOUGLAS* was fetched over from Eaton quarries in Leicestershire, still bearing *PARK GATE IRON & STEEL CO LTD* on its engine cover; but her mere 80 horsepower could only manage two wagons at a time against the steamer's seven (eight at a pinch) and ironically a contract was obtained to supply calcine to Skinningrove and other works at the rate of 400 tons a week with the expectation that it would be increased. Two excavators (the 43RB already mentioned and a 10RB clamshell moved moved here from Desborough) were used alternately at the three clamps, and *LAMPORT No. 3* put to work again one or two hours a day, though *DOUGLAS* did help out sometimes. Incidentally, while all the steamers faced Brixworth, the diesel faced Lamport. The Skinningrove contract seems to have been terminated before long, and the whole site assumed an abandoned air, with grass and weeds growing over the rusty tracks, and the corrugated iron buildings showing signs of rust and neglect, as did the engines inside — yet they were given plant numbers in the style of Stewarts & Lloyds Minerals Ltd, of whom Staveley Minerals was a subsidiary. These were *8310/19-21* respectively for *ROBERT, LAMPORT No. 2* and *3*, and *8311/40* for *DOUGLAS. HARTINGTON* had already gone by then. There was a caretaker management.

In the spring of 1968 a rough road was laid from the derelict yard of Brixworth station to the calcine banks, parallel with BR, so that lorries could be loaded with calcined ore directly, and it was thought that the familiar phrase 'rail traffic ceased' would be applicable. However, by an odd turn of fate this was not the case and the Lamport sidings came in for a final spell of frenzied activity from the week before Christmas 1968. The reason for this was said to be that the heavy autumn rains were causing problems in some quarries from which Stanton ironworks were obtaining their supplies of ore, and they ordered 2000 tons of calcine per week to tide them over. *LAMPORT No. 3* was put back in service, working two days a week marshalling trains of ore; on 11th March 1969 she stopped work with a blown mudhole cover — and that was the end of steam working at Lamport. *DOUGLAS* was put back into service for a while, but rail traffic ceased altogether in the summer and all further removals from the calcine bank were taken away by lorry, P. Partrick & Sons Ltd of Stanwick having the

Lamport Quarries (Staveley). The abandoned yard c June 1970, with the locomotive shed (centre) and weigh house (left). *LAMPORT No. 2* is in front of the water tank. The line to the quarries ran up the hillside in front of the piece of woodland.   (J. Bailey)

Lamport Quarries (Staveley).
Scaldwell yard, 22nd September 1977. The buildings were then occupied by Crawshaw, Robbins & Co Ltd. Loco shed (centre) and office (right).   (Eric Tonks)

contract. This ore was not only for ironworks, some going to cement works at Chinnor and Ketton, and also for roadmaking. The surviving track was lifted. The plates were removed from the steamers for safekeeping and three of the locomotives were sold for preservation, the exception being *LAMPORT No. 2*, cut up in desultory fashion by a scrap merchant in the period May-August 1970. The steamers have since moved—as preserved locomotives have a habit of doing—but are still extant; but the diesel *DOUGLAS*, undoubtedly the most interesting of the stock from the mechanical point of view, though hardly a 'native', was later sold for scrap by the owner. The locomotive shed was demolished in August 1971 but traces of the layout and building bases were still visible.

If one tours Brixworth Ironstone site and them moves over to Lamport, one is very conscious of how much there is to be seen at the former and how little at the latter—simply because restoration was obligatory at Lamport. Nevertheless, some things are to be seen here and there. Starting at Scaldwell, buildings in use by Crawshaw, Robbins & Co Ltd include the former locomotive shed, workshops and offices; the shed was rebuilt in 1985 with modern cladding, and new buildings of similar style were erected alongside, but the workshops were still of green corrugated iron. Across the road traces can just be discerned of the concrete base of the ropeway angle station. Between Scaldwell and Holcot Road the course of the line has been very effectively erased, even the site of the tipping area being levelled off (John R. Billows Ltd carried out this work); of the former ungated level crossing on the Scaldwell-Brixworth road nothing is to be seen at all. As one approaches Holcot Road, a row of Lombardy poplars will be observed in the grounds of a house built at the junction, and these trees feature in a number of photographs; somehow one did not expect them to be a mile away from the yard! It is worth examining the Holcot Road bridge, which is typical of the system, and of no other ironstone quarry; of red brick, with two layers of blue brick along the top, and at each end a capstone of concrete that can be described as half a shallow pyramid with the flat face facing the road. The red bricks were apparently of poor weather resistance and have been heavily mortared over at some stage (compare with the bridge on the Scaldwell-Hanging Houghton road, which has had no mortaring and the bricks are very badly pitted as a result). Peering over the north parapet brings no cutting into view, but the course of the line is clear nonetheless, as the filling has sunk over the years and the grass is greener than the surrounding area; the ground here has probably been undisturbed since 1963, but on the south side there are no similar indications. Crops have been grown in the area, though there is still much pasture crossed by replacement fences or hedges (hawthorn and elder, which seems to be typical of restored areas). More tangible remains are to be seen from the track to Grange Farm—depressions across the fields on each side, and the bridge more or less intact, though filled in on the east side, showing the stepped ironstone blocks, concrete lintel with ironstone blocks above and wooden parapet. The fields are sunken up to the road and some wire fences present. Of the course of the line to Brixworth ('Spratton') pit nothing can be seen, and the actual quarrying area has been largely built upon.

Evidence of the Hanging Houghton quarries is of similar degree. The bridge under the A508 to New Bridge pit (narrow gauge) has disappeared entirely, but of the standard gauge bridge the western parapet remains, and both those on the Scaldwell-Hanging Houghton road, with, between the two bridges, a conifer plantation on the belt of land between the former railway site and the road. Lower level ground can be seen on both sides of the A508 where quarrying has occurred in the past, that north of the drive to Hanging Houghton Lodge being cultivated; but there is little trace of Isham South pit, the route to which went apparently east of the Lodge. At the upper terminus of operating, opposite Faxton Grange, there is little to be seen apart from the slight lowering of the ground—and the level crossing was never started.

At the outlet end, the narrow gauge was originally extended along an artificial embankment, pierced to accommodate the ropeway bunkers, but parts were destroyed to make way for the standard gauge line. Of the latter no traces are discernible but can faintly be seen in aerial photographs—but

Lamport Quarries (Staveley). Parapet of the bridge over the line to New Bridge pit, on the Northampton-Market Harborough road, 13th October 1985. Note how the bricks have crumbled.

(A. Cocklin)

Lamport Quarries (Staveley). View over the parapet of the Holcot Road bridge, looking towards Scaldwell, 22nd September 1977. The course of the line is denoted by the darker vegetation. (Eric Tonks)

Lamport Quarries (Staveley). Bridge under the drive to Grange Farm, looking east, 22nd September 1977. Note the ironstone faces on each side. This was Holcot pit. (Eric Tonks)

Lamport Quarries (Staveley). *HANDYMAN* in June 1987 at the Midland Railway Trust site. After purchase for preservation in 1964, this locomotive was moved from place to place, but no one appeared to be much interested in restoring her. (A. Cocklin)

the end of the narrow gauge embankment is still there, planted with conifers forming a rather curious hump on the hillside, down which some traces of pylon bases can be seen. The standard gauge yard at Lamport was a shambles in 1977, with just one ruinous weigh-hut remaining. The whole area was churned up out of all recognition by vehicles dealing with the calcine, by then almost completely exhausted. In 1980 John R. Billows Ltd cleared the calcine site and it has returned to agricultural use, including the lorry road, which, however, still remains against the Brixworth Ironstone site.

Footnote

1 Rev. K. Kershaw, *Scaldwell Notebook & Scrapbook*; Northamptonshire Record Office.

Grid References

740731	Junction with LNWR
741731	Ropeway unloading point
753730	Ropeway bridge over main road

Hanging Houghton Quarries
752730	Locomotive shed
751730	Tipping stage
750730	Tramway terminus
753729	Bridge under main road
758728	New Bridge

Scaldwell Quarries
767722	Locomotive shed
763707	Bridge under Holcot Road
778698	Terminus by Reservoir
775700	Bridge by Grange Farm
766720	Transfer to s.g.
764721	S.g. level crossing of Scaldwell Road
741727	Calcine Banks (south end)

Locomotives

Scaldwell Quarries
Gauge; 3ft. 0in.

SCALDWELL	0-6-0ST	OC	P	1316	1913	11 x 16in.	2ft. 9in.	New 5/1913	(1)
BANSHEE	0-6-0ST	OC	MW	1276	1894	9 x 14in.	2ft. 6in.	(a)	(2)
			Reb	MW	1910				
HANDYMAN	0-4-0ST	OC	HC	573	1900	10 x 16in.	2ft.9½in.	(b)	(3)
LAMPORT	0-6-0ST	OC	P	1315	1913	11 x 16in.	2ft. 9in.	(c)	Scr 1/1964

(a) ex Eastwell Iron Ore Co Ltd by 1928.
(b) ex Cranford Ironstone Co Ltd, 1936.
(c) ex Hanging Houghton Quarries 1944.

(1) to Eastwell Iron Ore Co Ltd 1947; ex Eastwell 8/1950; to Narrow Gauge Railway Society, Brockham, Surrey 3/1964.
(2) to Hanging Houghton Quarries c 1936; ex Hanging Houghton c 1943. Scr 1945. Parts to Loddington Ironstone Co Ltd c 1951.
(3) to Welshpool & Llanfair Railway Preservation Society 5/1964.

Hanging Houghton Quarries
Gauge; 3ft. 0in.

LAMPORT	0-6-0ST	OC	P	1315	1913	11 x 16in.	2ft. 9in.	New 5/1913	(1)
BANSHEE	0-6-0ST	OC	MW	1276	1894	9 x 14in.	2ft. 6in.	(a)	(2)
			Reb	MW	1910				

(a) ex Scaldwell Quarries c 1936.

(1) to Scaldwell Quarries 1944.
(2) to Scaldwell Quarries c 1943.

Lamport Calcine Sidings; also Hanging Houghton Quarries, 1942-67
Gauge; 4ft. 8½in.

ROBERT	0-6-0ST	OC	AE	2068	1923	15 x 20in.	3ft. 6in.	New 1933	(1)
LAMPORT No. 2	0-6-0ST	OC	WB	2669	1942	15 x 22in.	3ft. 4½in.	New 7/1942	Scr 6/1970
LAMPORT No. 3	0-6-0ST	OC	WB	2670	1942	15 x 22in.	3ft. 4½in.	New 7/1942	(2)
HARTINGTON	0-6-0ST	OC	AE	1869	1921	15 x 20in.	3ft. 6in.	(a)	(3)
DOUGLAS	0-4-0DM	JF		21086	1936	52hp		(b)	(4)

(a) ex Staveley Ironworks 2/1961.
(b) ex Mill Hill Quarries, Leicestershire 12/1965.

(1) to London Railway Preservation Society 9/1969; stored at London Road Garage (Loughton) Ltd, Bletchely until moved to Quainton Road c 3/1970.
(2) to CEGB Leicester Power Station, 12/1969; stored for Leicester Industrial Locomotive Group; to Main Line Steam Trust, Loughborough 4/1973.
(3) to Desborough Quarries 5/1965.
(4) to Hunt & Co (Hinckley) Ltd 5/1970.

Quarry Machines

No. 20	S. Navvy. Long Jib Rail	RH	623	1920	1½ Cu.Yds.	58ft.	New 12/1920	(1)
No. 4	PP. Dragline/Shovel	RH	1167	1927			(a)	(2)
460	DE. Combined Shovel and Dragline	R)R	195	1934	1½ Cu.Yds.	27ft. 8in.	New 1934	(3)
No. 8	S. Shovel/dragline	RP	496	1917	1½ Cu.Yds.	25ft.	(b)	(4)
No. 20	S. Combined Shovel and Grab	RH	649	1920	2¾ Cu.Yds.	26ft.	(c)	(5)
No. 8	S. Shovel. Rail	RH	538	1919	1¼ Cu.Yds.	25ft.	(d)	(6)
No. 4	SND. Transporter	RH	539	1919			(d)	(7)
21RB	D. Shovel	RB	2860	1935	¾ Cu.Yd.	18ft. 6in.	New 10/1935	(8)
21RB	D. Shovel	RB	3118	1936			New 8/1936	(9)
43RB	D. Dragline	RB	4383	1939	1 Cu.Yd.	70ft.	New 4/1939	(10)
43RB	D. Shovel	RB	6747	1942	1¾ Cu.Yds.	22ft.	New 4/1942	(11)
43RB	D. Dragline	RB	6748	1942	1 Cu. Yd.	70ft.	New 5/1942	(12)
10RB	D. Dragline/Clamshell	RB	6750	1942	5½ Cu.ft. (grab)	35ft.	New 6/1942	(13)
55RB	E. Dragline	RB	6749	1942	4 Cu.Yds.	60ft.	New 11/1942	(14)
10RB	D. Clamshell digger	RB	6840	1943	5/6 Cu.Yds.	35ft.	(e)	(15)

(a) ex ?.
(b) ex Charwelton Quarries c 1934.
(c) ex Sproxton Quarries 4/1935.
(d) ex Kettering Iron & Coal Co Ltd 7/1935.
(e) ex Desborough Quarries 1962.

(1) At Isham South pit; to Holcot pit; to Brixworth pit. To Thos. W. Ward Ltd for scrap 1953.

(2) At Preslands pit; to Holcot pit. To Pitsford Quarries c 1932; ret. To Cranford Quarries 1952.

(3) At New Bridge pit. Scr 1969.

(4) At Holcot pit; to Brixworth pit. To Eaton Basic Quarries 1942.

(5) At Holcot pit. To Sproxton Quarries 1/1938.

(6) At Garretts pit. To Thos. W. Ward Ltd for scrap 1945.

(7) At Garretts pit. Scr 1941.

(8) New to Holcot pit; to New Bridge pit. To Pitsford Quarries c 1960.

(9) At Holcot pit; to Brixworth pit. To Loddington Quarries; ret. To Cranford Quarries.

(10) At Holcot pit. s/s.

(11) At New Bridge pit. To Easton Basic Quarries 1965.

(12) Special bucket for use with calcine. s/s c 1970.

(13) To Cranford Quarries 1948.

(14) Probably at New Bridge pit. To calcine bank. To Cranford Quarries 2/1948.

(15) At calcine clamps. To Cranford Quarries c 1965.

LAMPORT QUARRIES

Owners: Glendon Iron Co: Glendon Iron Co Ltd from 23rd June 1886.

This was another early venture but a short-lived one, being opened for production in 1882 and closed in 1890 when the company shut down its furnaces at Finedon; existing indications, however, stamp the rail system as one of more than average solidarity, comprising a standard gauge line from the goods yard of Lamport station to the pits lying west of the road through Lamport village, a shallow valley enabling the route to be fairly easily graded. The brick-built weighhouse for wagons and the roomy locomotive shed lay some 450 yards from the junction, on the outskirts of a spinney bordering the stream alongside; but details of the locomotive and rolling stock have unfortunately eluded research. The quarrying area, as indicated on the plans in Northamptonshire Record Office, was less than five acres.

The buildings mentioned, converted to farm use, are still recognisable and can be seen from the station site. The course of the tramway is not perceptible but the site of quarrying is marked by a crescent-shaped depression in the ground corresponding with the tramway route depicted on the 1884 OS map, and presumably represents the final gullet. It may be seen from the roadside up the hill from the stream and in 1977 was a field of maize.

Grid References

761751	Terminus of line
754753	Locomotive shed

Lamport Quarries (Glendon). The long abandoned locomotive shed, c 1953. The occupant of this shed has not been identified. (G. H. Starmer)

EXPLANATION OF TABLES

Locomotives

The columns show in order:- title: type:cylinder position: maker: maker's number: year built: cylinder dimensions: driving wheel diameter: origin: disposal. In referring to these columns the following points should be noted.

Title. Unofficial names used by the staff but not carried by the engine are denoted by inverted commas.

Type. The Whyte system of wheel classification is used, but if wheels are not connected by outside rods they are shown as 4w, 6w as the case may be. The following abbreviations are used:

T	Side Tank	DM	Diesel Mechanical	BE	Battery Electric
PT	Pannier Tank	DE	Diesel Electric	WE	Wire Electric
ST	Saddle Tank	DH	Diesel Hydraulic		
WT	Well Tank	PM	Petrol Mechanical		
VB	Vertical Boiler	PE	Petrol Electric		
G	Geared	PMR	Petrol Mechanical Railcar		

Cylinder Position

IC Inside Cylinders
OC Outside Cylinders
VC Vertical Cylinders

Makers. The following abbreviations are used, with lesser known builders' names being given in full.

AB	Andrew Barclay Sons & Co Ltd, Kilmarnock.
AE	Avonside Engine Co Ltd, Bristol
AP	Aveling & Porter Ltd, Rochester
B	Barclays & Co, Kilmarnock
BEV	British Electric Vehicles Ltd, Southport
Bg	E. E. Baguley Ltd, Burton on Trent
BH	Black Hawthorn & Co Ltd, Gateshead
Bton	Brighton Locomotive Works, LB&SCR
CF	Chapman & Furneaux Ltd, Gateshead
DC	Drewry Car Co Ltd, London (Suppliers only)
DK	Dick, Kerr & Co Ltd, Preston
EE	English Electric Co Ltd, Preston
EV	Ebbw Vale Steel Coal & Iron Co Ltd, Ebbw Vale
FE	Falcon Engine & Car Works Ltd, Loughborough
FH	F. C. Hibberd & Co Ltd, London
FW	Fox Walker & Co, Bristol
GB	Greenwood & Batley Ltd, Leeds

224

GEC/USA	General Electric Co, USA
H	James & Frederick Howard Ltd, Bedford
HC	Hudswell Clarke & Co Ltd, Leeds
HCR	Hudswell Clarke & Rodgers, Leeds
HE	Hunslet Engine Co Ltd, Leeds
HL	Hawthorn Leslie & Co Ltd, Newcastle upon Tyne
Hu	Robert Hudson Ltd, Leeds
JF	John Fowler & Co (Leeds) Ltd
K	Kitson & Co Ltd, Leeds
KE	Kilmarnock Engineering Co Ltd
KS	Kerr, Stuart & Co Ltd, Stoke on Trent
Mkm	Markham & Co Ltd, Chesterfield
MR	Motor Rail Ltd, Bedford
MW	Manning Wardle & Co Ltd, Leeds
N	Neilson & Co, Glasgow
OK	Orenstein & Koppel AG, Berlin
P	Peckett & Sons Ltd, Bristol
RH	Ruston & Hornsby Ltd, Lincoln
RR	Rolls Royce Ltd, Shrewsbury
RS	Robert Stephenson & Co Ltd, Newcastle upon Tyne and Darlington
RSH	Robert Stephenson & Hawthorns Ltd, Newcastle upon Tyne
S	Sentinel (Shrewsbury) Ltd
Sdn	Swindon Locomotive Works, GWR
SS	Sharp Stewart & Co Ltd, Glasgow
VF	Vulcan Foundry Ltd, Newton-le-Willows
WB	W. G. Bagnall Ltd, Stafford
YE	Yorkshire Engine Co Ltd, Sheffield

Maker's Number. Reb = Rebuilt.

Year Built. The year quoted is that given on the maker's plate, or from the maker's records if the date does not appear on the plate.

Cylinder and Driving Wheel Dimensions. These apply to locomotive as new.

Origin. 'New' indicates that the locomotive was delivered by the makers to this location at the stated date (to the month where known). Transfers from elsewhere are indicated by a bracketed letter and appropriate footnote.

Disposal. Locomotives transferred to another owner or site are shown by a bracketed number with corresponding footnote. Scr = Scrapped. s/s = scrapped or sold, disposal unknown.

Explanation of tables

Quarry Machines

The information is set out in much the same way as for locomotives, but as collected information on quarry machines has not appeared before we give rather more in the way of explanation. The columns show in order:- title (if any): class description: power source and type of machine: maker: maker's number: year built: bucket capacity: jib or boom length: origin: disposal.

Title. Often machines carried no title, but major operators such as Stewarts & Lloyds Minerals Ltd gave them numbers, quoted where known; and a very few were named.

Class Description. Steam machines were most commonly referred to as '10-ton', '20-ton', etc, the 'ton' referring not to the weight but to the cutting pressure on the bucket teeth. Ruston Proctor & Co Ltd adopted these as class numbers, a No. 20 machine being a '20-ton' and so on, and these class numbers have been used in the tables, as in the manufacturer's literature. Whitaker's used a letter code but unfortunately only in a few cases do we know these, so we have had to fall back on '12 ton' etc. Ruston & Hornsby Ltd used designatory numbers for larger machines, e.g. No. 250.

Diesel and electric machines were given class numbers by Ruston Bucyrus Ltd from a scheme used by the Bucyrus Co. The early machines were described as 37B, 43B etc but this was later changed to 37RB and 43RB etc, and we have used the latter throughout for simplicity. The numbers correspond roughly with the weight of the machine in tons. Ransomes & Rapier Ltd applied class numbers such as 422, 480 etc, and also used these numbers for steam machines of the same power. The large Walking Draglines of both manufacturers incorporated 'W' in the class description—3W, 5W for RB in ascending order of size, and W 150, W 1400 etc for R&R, the numbers again corresponding roughly to the weights.

Power Source and Type of Machine. The power source is indicated by a letter:-
S—Steam: D—Diesel: DE—Diesel Electric: E—Electric: PP—Petrol-paraffin.

The two main types of machine are shovels and draglines. In simple terms, the latter were used primarily for removing overburden by dragging the bucket up the working face by a chain in a scraping motion, then slewing the bucket round to dump the load on the worked-out area; a shovel would then dig out the ore beneath. Obviously there are many variants on these according to circumstances, and digger drivers were very adept in using their machines in difficult positions. Some removal of overburden was done by 'stripping shovels' of large size. The form and duties of various specialized machines will be obvious from their names—crane, clamshell, back-acter, etc. Some machines were rail-mounted, some on crawlers or 'Caterpillar' tracks. When the type of machine is uncertain, the term 'navvy' is used.

Makers. The following abbreviations are used, with lesser known builder's names being given in full.

226

At	Atlantic Equipment Co, USA
BE	Bucyrus-Erie Co, USA
Berry	Henry Berry & Co Ltd, Leeds
Bu	Bucyrus Co, USA
Lima	Baldwin Lima Hamilton Co, USA
Marion	Marion Steam Shovel Co, USA
NBM	Newton, Bean & Mitchell, Bradford
Priestman	Priestman Brothers Ltd, Hull
RB	Ruston Bucyrus Ltd, Lincoln
RH	Ruston & Hornsby Ltd, Lincoln
RP	Ruston Proctor & Co Ltd, Lincoln
R&R	Ransomes & Rapier Ltd, Ipswich
S&P	Stothert & Pitt Ltd, Bath
Taylor Hubbard	Taylor Hubbard & Co Ltd, Leicester
Wh	Whitaker Bros Ltd, Leeds
Wilson	John H. Wilson & Co Ltd, Liverpool

Makers' Number and **Year Built.** These are taken from manufacturers' records in the case of the Ruston companies and from R & R; from operators' records otherwise.

Bucket Capacity and **Jib or Boom Length.** The figures come from operators' records mostly, sometimes from manufacturers. There is no hard and fast rule about the terms 'jib' and 'boom' but generally steam machines are spoken of as having jibs, and diesel and electric machines booms, particularly the larger machines.

Origin. 'New' means that the machine was supplied by the makers to this location. The months quoted are those shown as delivery dates in the makers' records; but very often machines were supplied in sections to be assembled on site (this being particularly so with large machines) so that some time elapsed before they entered service.

Transfers from other locations are shown by bracketed letters and appropriate footnotes. To save space, these footnotes also include details of any changes in bucket capacity or jib length.

Disposal. A machine transferred to another location is shown by a bracketed number and corresponding footnote. Scr = scrapped: s/s = scrapped or sold, disposal unknown. These footnotes also include known details of the individual quarries or working faces that the machine served in the system concerned, with dates where known.

Sources of Information. The principal sources of information consulted and quoted from, using the abbreviations given, are as follows. All were published by Her/His Majesty's Stationery Office.

Mineral Statistics of Great Britain. Robert Hunt.	1853-81	(MS)
Mineral Statistics of Great Britain. Geological Survey Memoirs	1882-94	(MS)
List of Quarries in the United Kingdom and the Isle of Man	1895-1934	(LQ)
Special Reports on the Mineral Resources of Great Britain:		
Part XII—Iron Ore. Geologial Survey Memoirs	1920	(GSM)
The Mesozoic Ironstone of England: The Northampton		
Sand Ironstone	1951	(NSI)
The Mesozoic Ironstone of England: The Liassic Ironstones	1952	(LI)

INDEX

Index